MW00635814

2017.2.21

陳 嘉 生 Jason C. S. Chen

茶山紀行
A Tea Lover's Travel Diary

TeaMaster 茶馬仕

A TeaMaster Book
Seattle

Publisher's Cataloging-In-Publication Data
(Prepared by The Donohue Group, Inc.)

Chen, Chiashen.
Cha shan ji xing / Chen Chiashen = A tea lover's travel diary / Jason C.S.
Chen. -- 1st ed.

p. : chiefly col. ill. ; cm.

In Chinese and English.
ISBN: 978-0-9826540-0-2

1. Tea--China--Pictorial works. 2. Tea gardens--China--Pictorial works.
3. Tea trade--China. 4. Chen, Chiashen--Diaries.
5. C.C. Fine Tea Company. I. Title. II. Title: A tea lover's travel diary

SB272.C5 C45 2010
633/.72/0951

First Edition : October 2010
Printed in China

謹以此書獻給我親愛的父母

I am happy to dedicate this book to my dear parents.

序言

D. Major Cohen (梅杰 柯恩)

　　我很榮幸並以謙虛之心為好友、茶師父 Jason Chen (陳嘉生) 美好的新書分享一些想法。身處兩位茶界的巨人，James Norwood Pratt （詹姆士　諾木派迪）及 Jason Chen，我自認只是個受到鼓勵的學徒，其中 Jason Chen 有益的知識，良好的耐心及大方的人格，給我很特別指引。

　　當我移居西雅圖，開始為星巴克咖啡公司教育部門工作，不久之後就認識 Jason，他是以朋友及供應商的身份，經由星巴克的茶公司 Tazo 介紹。我一直記得與 Jason 第一次品嚐的茗茶 - 白毫銀針 - 至今都是我最喜愛的茶。當我離開他在西雅圖的辦事處時，心靈上彷如得到珍貴之禮 - 我的感官依然保留著甜味，想像第一次前往我夢想的國度旅行，印象中有綠色春之花園以及靈巧之手忙碌著，不同凡響的茶與美麗的茶具，都依古老的方法在製作，而我只能認出少部份的名字。迄今我和 Jason 品茗多次，傾聽他的見聞，看過千百張他從旅途中的攝影，並且與他常年共事，如獲佳禮，也是我最珍惜的友誼。現在他的第二本書，將呈現他所獲得的精華，並且特許我們亦友亦師去了解他：靈光獨耀的視野及開闊大氣之特質，証實了他對茶的熱愛。謝謝你吾友，"茶悅人生"。

有關 D.Major Cohen (梅杰 柯恩) 簡介

　　Major Cohen 目前是星巴克咖啡公司國際發展部門，資深專案設計經理，他在 1995 年加入星巴克，當時他是半職的咖啡調製師。對于茶與咖啡的探索可追溯到 1970 年代，在加入星巴克之前 Major 擔任過波士頓地區學校教師，藝術部門主管，當地的企業家，及從事商業攝影 19 年；他的攝影作品在 Boston(波士頓)，Cambridge(劍橋)，Rochester (羅契斯特)，New York (紐約) and Seattle (西雅圖) 等城市展出。

　　Major 祖藉新英格蘭；他喜愛單人划漿，並與密友 Anne 及收養的流浪狗 Koby 共渡時光。

Foreword
by D. Major Cohen

I am honored and humbled to share a few thoughts of introduction to this wonderful new book by my friend and Tea Master, Jason Chen. Among two giants of tea, James Norwood Pratt and Jason Chen, I acknowledge an inspired apprenticeship, one that has especially been guided by Jason's significant knowledge, great patience and immense generosity of spirit.

I met Jason not long after I arrived in Seattle to work on coffee education for Starbucks Coffee. He was introduced as a friend and supplier of our tea company, Tazo Tea. I remember the first tea we enjoyed, still one of my most favorite – Yin Zhen Bai Hao (Silver Needle White Tea). I left his offices in downtown Seattle feeling inspired by having received great gifts -- the tastes of teas still sweetening my palette, images of travel to places I dreamt of experiencing first hand, impressions of lush green spring gardens and nimble hands at work, of ancient steps being followed to create extraordinary tea and beautiful tea vessels – to name just a few. I have sat with Jason for many hours since - listened to his stories, looked at thousands of images from his travels, and even traveled with him in China. The gifts he has given me and many of my colleagues and friends are deeply cherished. Now in this, his second book, he has captured the essence of what he gives to those of us privileged to know him as our teacher and friend: a glimpse of his extraordinary vision and a generous physical manifestation of his love for tea. Thank you my friend, "tea makes a happy day".

About Major: Major is currently a sr. design project manager with Starbucks coffee's global development team. While he began his journey with Starbucks in 1995 as a part-time barista, his coffee and tea learning goes back to Coffee Connection days in the early 1970's. Major was a school teacher, art department head, local entrepreneur and worked as commercial photographer in Boston for 19 years prior to joining Starbucks. His photographic work has been exhibited in Boston, Cambridge, Rochester, New York and Seattle.

Major is a New England native who enjoys rowing a single shell and spending time with his partner, Anne, and their adopted dog, Koby.

Jason Chen（陳嘉生）—— 茶師父介紹

James Norwood Pratt(詹姆士 諾木 派迪)

　　非常榮幸在此介紹這本書，這是一位藝術家所做的藝術工作，當Jason Chen(陳嘉生)由台灣移民美國，跟隨他的是中國文化與藝術，最有價值的是他的心靈與智慧，而不是豐富的行李；書法及藝術豐富了他在美國的生活，同時也成為一個瓷器、竹器藝術產品的設計者，而大部份的時間他獲得一個古老的尊稱"茶師父"。茶性清明和靜，當我們品茶時可以得到內心清靜的境界，而我到目前為止還沒有遇到一位內心清靜，並且如此深入了解茶的人如同Jason Chen一樣。

　　您所專注捧閱的這本書，將帶領我們儘可能的貼近，兩種偉大定位的烏龍茶之製作藝術，"鳳凰單欉"及"安溪鐵觀音"，這必需感謝JasonChen的父親，在台灣送給他相機，而從此JasonChen帶著相機旅行，包括中國茶園與美國之間將近200次的遠行。這相機將帶領我們拜訪中國廣東省東北部鳳凰山區，透過鏡頭我們看到了神奇古老的生產秘密。

　　單欉技幹 - 不是灌木- ，這我們所看到的景像，己在雲霧中挺立久遠，從宋朝迄今春日循環已有八個世紀，單欉品種只能在此地生長，每株平均年產量約為20磅，雖然鳳凰山區腹地廣大，但是老單欉的數量有限，產量也是有限，而且從不快速生產，如此特別的茶真是帶給世界的禮物，吾人需心懷感謝擁有如此茗茶，不可貪求。而Jason用相機以尊敬的心觀察茶廠的生產過程，從鮮葉採摘到完成，包括：萎凋、作菁、殺菁、條揉、烘焙等。

　　這裏的農業生產過程是崇高地藝術工作，如同它有所具有之鮮爽、濃洌、蜂密香氣，除了親身經驗體會，無法勉強描述，只有少部份的人品嗜到真正的鳳凰單欉 - Jason 如此告訴我們，但是透過鏡頭，他展示給我們，這個不同凡響的茶真正的製作技術。

不同于鳳凰單欉,鐵觀音是中國知名度最高和最多人品嚐的烏龍茶,而最好的鐵觀音只生產于中國福建省安溪閩南地區,此地有多種鐵觀音茶樹,但只有最好的製茶師生產真正的好茶, Jason 透過鏡頭為我們解開原因 – 每斤好茶都是數十小時連續不停止的製茶工藝生產,想像每斤茶經過重複加水浸泡,可以沖泡出600杯茶,我們需感謝這大量的手工藝術工作,而吾人只用少量的昂貴就獲得世界上最大的奢華。傳統的安溪鐵觀音就像傳統的古巴Habano (哈巴諾)雪茄,必需生產在Vuelta Abajo 地區。在古巴很多地區生產雪茄,正如同鐵觀音也有很多產地,包括中國其他的地區,但只有少數被大家公認,而且沒有一種可以超越外緊結形,品質精美的安溪鐵觀音。

　　在這本茶山記行,Jason發現並且深思有關安溪地區傳統鐵觀音的改變:"不禁惋惜鐵觀音數百年來精湛、完美、獨到的工藝將可能消失"幸運地,Jason以自己的觀察用相機為我們保存了傳統的生產方法。(而其他人亦將會相隨)

　　另一個值得慶幸,Jason能夠與我們分享已有得獎紀錄的製茶工藝;1997年他在Seattle (西雅圖) 創立的C.C.Fine Tea CO.(茶馬仕茶業有限公司)不只是在中國培育及生產有機茶,同時也銷售高品質茶葉給美國的愛茶者,就像我們一樣具有敏銳品茶能力人仕。多年以來C.C.Fine Tea CO.已在中國的烏龍茶比賽多次得獎,看過這本茶山記行,您將不再懷疑。

有關James Norwood Pratt(詹姆士 諾木 派迪) 簡介
　　不論是担任過美國第一家傳統中國茶館的榮譽董事,或是榮任印度第一屆茶葉比賽的評審。James Norwood Pratt 多年來均以作者、編輯、推廣者、教師等身份從事于茶,他主要的編著 "James Norwood Pratt's Tea Dictionary" (詹姆士 諾木 派迪 的茶字典) 將在2010年出版問世,這可能是世界上有關茶及逸聞,最廣泛及可信賴的閱讀著作。 目前他與他的妻子Valerie Turner 同住在美國舊金山。

Introducing Jason Chen, Tea Master
by James Norwood Pratt

It is quite an honor to introduce a book by an artist that's about works of art. When he immigrated to the US, Jason Chen brought with him from his native Taiwan a wealth of Chinese art and culture, riches he carried not in his luggage but in his head and heart. Ever since, he has enriched life in America as a calligrapher and artist, as a designer and producer of artifacts in porcelain and bamboo, and most of all as one worthy of the ancient title "Tea Master." Tea is quiet and makes a quietness inside as we savor it. I have met no one who enters that quietness and understands tea more deeply than Jason Chen.

This book you hold--and behold--will bring us as close as we can get to the heart of two towering monuments to the oolong tea maker's art, Phoenix Mountain and Anxi Tie Kuan Yin. This is thanks to the camera Jason's father bought him in Taiwan which Jason has never been without on any of his almost 200 trips back and forth to China's tea lands. With this camera he takes us to visit the rugged and remote Phoenix Mountains of northeastern Guangdong province and allows us to join him as eyewitnesses to ancient magic.

The single-trunk tea trees—not shrubs—we see silhouetted against the mist are themselves often centuries old—the offspring of plants already ancient in the Song dynasty eight centuries ago. This single trunk ("Dan Cong") varietal is found nowhere else nor is tea like it produced anywhere but here, at a rate of perhaps 20 pounds of made tea per leaf-yielding tree per year. Phoenix Mountain is vast but the number of her tea trees is finite and their yield cannot be increased, nor production hurried. Such a unique tea is a gift to the world and it is for us to be grateful for what we receive—not greedy for more. Jason's camera observes these leaves reverently from new shoots to harvest and then follows them through the painstaking processes of manufacture—the withering, the "dancing," and the repeated rollings, restings, and firings---the mystery entire.

Here is an agricultural product elevated to the status of a work of art. Like its fresh, strong and honey-sweet flavor, Phoenix Mountain oolong cannot be grasped except by experience. "Just a few people get a chance to taste it," Jason tells us, but as our camera-eye he is able to show us where this unique tea comes from and just what makes it the way it is.

Tie Kuan Yin, by contrast, is surely China's best known and most widely enjoyed oolong tea and China's best Tie Kuan Yin's are thought to be those produced in Anxi ("Sand County") in the Minnan sector of Fujian province. Here varietal Tie Kuan Yin is abundant, but the finest artisanal product remains rare. For us Jason's camera reveals the reason—the endless hours of skillful labor that go into every single jin of made tea. Considering that each jin (i.e., "pound") with repeated infusions yields perhaps 600 cups, this largely hand-made work of art must be considered among the least expensive of the world's great luxuries. A classic Tie Kuan Yin from Anxi is like the classic Habano cigar from Cuba's revered Vuelta Abajo region. There are many cigars made in Cuba just as there are Tie Kuan Yin's of many origins, including Tie Kuan Yin's from many other places in China, but by common consent there are few to equal and none to surpass Anxi's at its tightly-rolled best.

In his travel diary, Jason muses on the changes he has seen in the region's tea traditions: "I feel pity that the delicate, perfect, special Tie Kuan Yin process developed over the past 300 plus years is almost gone." Jason's camera, fortunately, has preserved the old ways for us (and those who come after us) to witness what he himself has seen.

It is also our very good fortune that Jason enables us to share these works of art whose creation he documented on the spot. The C.C. Fine Tea Company he founded in Seattle in 1997 not only grows and manufactures organic teas in China but also sells the finest of these to discerning American tea lovers like us. Over the years quite a few C.C. Fine Tea Company oolongs have won China's highest awards in tea competitions. Look through this "Tea Lover's Travel Diary" you will not wonder why.

About JNP: Whether as Honorary Director of America's first traditional Chinese tea house or as International Juror of India's first-ever tea competition, James Norwood Pratt has served the cause of tea around the world for many years as author, editor, instigator and teacher. His landmark "James Norwood Pratt's Tea Dictionary" appeared in 2010. Possibly the world's most widely-read authority on tea and tea lore, he lives with his wife Valerie Turner in San Francisco.

茶与摄影

　　1974那年我19歲，家住台灣高雄，北上台北工作的前夕，父親帶我到高雄最大的照相器材行，選了一台相機送我，這個相機用了他一個月的薪資，這是我最珍貴的禮物之一，從此帶著這相機上山下海，他鄉旅行，留下許多風土人情，晨暉夕映美好記憶，這相機不但陪我成長，也幫助我打開了另一扇心門，透過鏡頭，看到恆變的美。

　　1997年我在西雅圖開始茶的事業，走遍了中國各地著名茶區，迄今往返台灣、中國、美國有一百六十餘趟，相機不但成工作上重要的工具，同時紀錄中國名茶、名種原產地的風貌，為了讓更多愛茶人仕，深入地了解原產茶園及生產過程，因此以感謝的心情，挑選單種名茶相關茶園風光、生產之攝影作品，配合簡潔的文字說明介紹，集結成冊出版，盼同好多多賜教！並祝願優良的中國名茶早日建立世界知名品牌。

陳嘉生 于西雅圖 2010-2-1

Tea and My Camera

In 1974 I was 19 years old. I was living in Kaohsiung, Taiwan. The next day I was beginning a new job in Taipei. My father took me to the biggest camera store in Kaohsiung. He picked out one camera for me. It cost him one month's salary. This camera became my treasure. Ever since, this camera is always with me, in the mountains, and at the seaside. The camera has provided many beautiful memories from the sea, the mountains, at sunrise and at sunset. That camera has been with me as I have moved through the years. It has always opened my mind through the pictures and the memories.

In 1997 I began my tea business in Seattle, Washington. By this time I had visited almost every famous tea garden in China. From Taiwan to China, from China to the United States, I have crossed the Pacific ocean more than 160 times. The camera has been an important business accessory. I have photographed many famous original Chinese tea gardens. In order for tea lovers to understand more about the Chinese tea process and tea gardens, I chose two very famous teas, tea gardens and processes, Tie Kuan Yin and Phoenix Single-Tree. This book will be followed by subsequent photographic diaries on other famous Chinese teas. We all know that one picture is worth 1,000 words. Each of these books will rely on the photographs to tell the story, with a few well-chosen words in support. This book is published for all tea lovers. Now, I hope you will comment on this book so I can learn more. Also I have a wish for the future and that is someday soon Chinese tea will develop a brand name known throughout the world.

Jason C.S. Chen
Tea Master

目录 Contents

Tie Kuan Yin
鐵觀音
A Tea Lover's Travel Diary

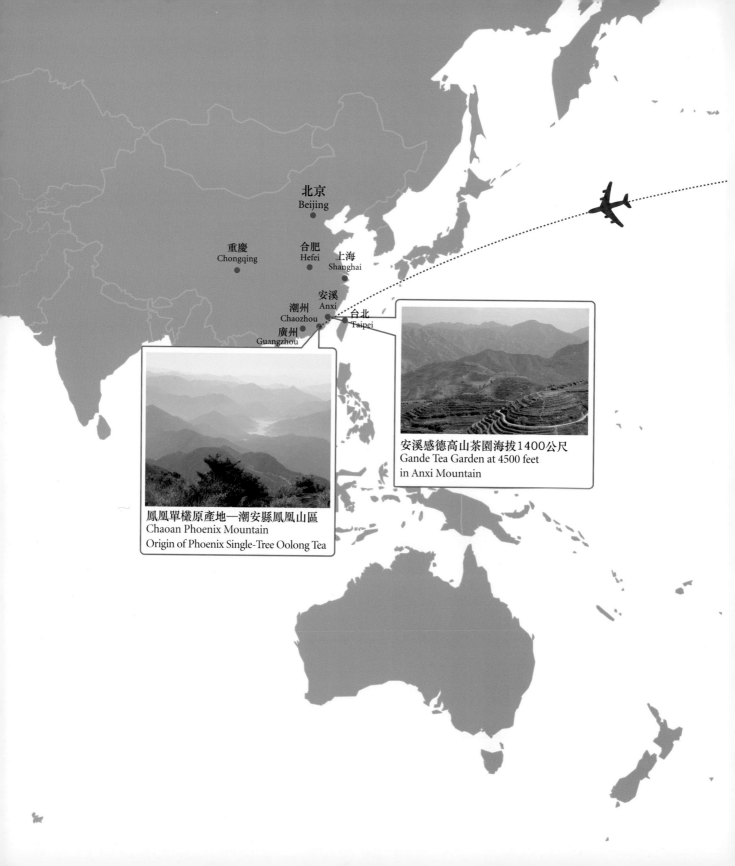

北京
Beijing

重慶
Chongqing

合肥
Hefei

上海
Shanghai

安溪
Anxi

潮州
Chaozhou

廣州
Guangzhou

台北
Taipei

安溪感德高山茶園海拔1400公尺
Gande Tea Garden at 4500 feet
in Anxi Mountain

鳳凰單欉原產地—潮安縣鳳凰山區
Chaoan Phoenix Mountain
Origin of Phoenix Single-Tree Oolong Tea

西雅圖
Seattle

舊金山
San Francisco

洛杉磯
Los Angeles

芝加哥
Chicago

紐約
New York

09/10

鳳凰單樅

Phoenix Single-Tree Oolong Tea

鳳凰茶山紀行

Phoenix Mountain Diary

2009年4月27日我剛結束杭州西湖龍井、安徽祁門紅茶、浙江有機毛峰綠茶的業務行程，隨即轉往廣東潮汕地區，拜訪慕名已久的鳳凰單欉。心情放鬆了，又有了新的期望，不是那麼興奮，卻又有些迫不及待。鳳凰單欉雖然盛名在外，名列中國十大名茶，卻因為地理位置、產品的稀有性、市場推廣方式，限制了愛茶人對單欉的了解。真正試得廬山真面目，品嚐到正宗品種、產地、地道傳統工序製作的人毛麟鳳角。

28日清晨即由潮州出發，車行在迂迴鄉間小路、盤旋在山間峽谷，地勢漸升高，約2小時後終於到達鳳凰小鎮，街上茶莊林立，純樸的市集對比四周環山的寧靜，有不一樣的繁忙，也透露這裏是單欉的家鄉。小車繼續緩緩地穿過市集，在烏崇嶺山腳下，終於會見了鳳凰單欉的專家鄭協龍先生，也才了解為什麼要安排車在山下接待的原因。據鄭先生介紹，真正的高山鳳凰單欉，茶園分佈在海拔1400尺的山嶺四周，由此地還要再驅車上山30分鐘才到達。換車之後隨即出發，山勢快速的攀升，景觀迅速的展開，層巒迭翠，山嵐飄渺，風景壯闊，訪茶人的心如鵬展翅，飛翔在鳳凰山之顛。

午時到達茶場，海拔1300公尺的曬青場上，正忙著鋪曬今天第一批的午時茶菁，高山上氣候涼爽，日照紫外線強烈，場上的製茶師傅穿著長袖夾克保暖，戴著草編寬帽防曬，製茶師說;鳳凰單欉茶菁有三不採-雨水、濃霧、烈陽均不採

摘，這些茶菁都是風和日麗天的午時茶菁，約30分鐘後就要移入廠內進行室內委凋，委凋過程約需10～12小時，包括:茶菁靜置、搖菁、浪菁、做菁，反復進行，有時需配合氣溫，為茶菁加被提溫，或勻堆降溫，使茶菁得到最均勻的萎凋，發酵後形成的綠葉紅鑲邊，散發出單欉特有的香氣，這是製作單欉茶最重要的一環，製茶師傅們莫不盡心護呵。

午後時分，製茶師傅們正在忙碌著室內委凋，我再前往更高處的茶園，當天約有二百五十個採茶師傅，大部份來自鄰近的福建省，性情敦厚開朗，樂觀敬業，手法熟練，採茶時伴著隱約悠長的歌聲，散落在山脊斜坡上。茶山上到處是百年茶樹，背山向陽，傍依著巨石、山泉生機勃然，挺拔翠綠。茶山上遍地是億萬年前火山爆發後形成的褐壤，有機層深厚，為單欉提供了特殊的養份。站在這座茶山—烏凍山高嶺，舉目遠眺，江山如畫，層峰遂遠，黛色無盡，此時我終於找到鳳凰單欉芬芳遠播，中外馳名的答案。

一、高海拔山區，優美的地理位置、適宜的氣候、及綠色環境。
二、800年來(宋朝)相續不斷的優良單欉品種。
三、傳統、嚴懂、完美的單欉製茶工藝。
四、擁有數十年豐富經驗的製茶師，合作無間的製茶團隊。
五、火山岩褐壤地貌，豐富的有機土層。

April 27, 2009

I had just finished a business trip for 3 different teas. The three teas: Westlake Dragonwell, Keemun Black, and Organic Mao Feng Green. This meant visiting three different provinces: Zhejiang, Jiangsu, and Anhui. Now I head to Guangdong province, Chaozhou area, located in Northeast Guangdong province. I am going to visit the famous Phoenix Single Tree area.

My mind is relaxed. The trip has been tiring, but I also have new hope, new expectations. I cannot wait to see this area. Phoenix Single Tree is so famous. It is one of the top ten teas in China. The region is not so convenient. The production is limited, and the tea is not often marketed properly. Because of this, most tea lovers cannot understand the real Phoenix Single Tree Oolong and just a few people get a chance to taste it.

April 28, 2009

Early in the morning I leave Chaozhou city. I have a small rental car with a driver. The country road is winding. The road climbs up. Then we reach Phoenix Mountain. After two hours, I finally arrive at a small town. On the main street, there are many tea stores. These shops are small and plain but busy. This is different from the city. Here, the view always includes a beautiful mountain. It is very easy to get the feeling that this is the hometown of authentic Phoenix Single Tree.

My little car keeps going through the small town to another peak, Oodong Mountain. At last, I meet Mr. Zheng. He is the Vice President of the Palm of Heaven Tea Company. Now, I understand why the owner asks me to wait for Mr. Zheng at the base of Oodong Mountain. Reaching the tea garden is not easy.

We change cars before continuing, moving to an SUV to go to a higher elevation. It takes about 30 minutes. Mr. Zheng tells me the real authentic high mountain Phoenix Single Tree tea garden is at 4,500 feet, the very top of Phoenix Mountain.

The last leg of the trip takes another 30 minutes. Now we arrive at the tea garden, itself. As we proceed up the mountain, the vista quickly grows. The view is tremendous. This huge mountain is rough and craggy. Misty clouds float around us, making the mountain seem even higher. The view is beautiful, deep, and wide, like the Grand Canyon. My mind soars in the sky above Phoenix Mountain like an eagle flying over the Phoenix Single Tree tea garden.

It is about noon when I arrive at the factory and tea garden. The elevation is about 4,500 feet. Many Tea Masters are busy with outdoor withering of the first tea picked for the day. The mountain weather is cool. The sun shines strongly in the thin air. The Tea Masters usually wear protective clothing and hats to shield them from the harsh mountain sunlight.

One of the Tea Masters tells me there are three conditions when Phoenix Single Tree should not be picked: rainy days, foggy days, and too much sun. This day is perfect for picking the fresh leaf.

The outdoor withering continues for 30 minutes. The first-picked leaves are moved in to begin indoor withering. Resting, rolling, dancing the leaves, and separating, are all part of the indoor withering process.

The weather is always a factor. If it is too cold, the leaves undergoing indoor withering must be covered with a blanket. When the weather is too hot, the leaves are separated again to cool them down. Many skills are required to produce even-fermentation and the best tea.

Indoor withering always takes 10-12 hours. Properly fermented fresh Phoenix Single Tree Oolong leaves are always green in the center and golden brown on the edges. Indoor withering is the most important part of the Phoenix Single Tree Oolong process. Each of the Tea Masters work very hard to properly prepare the leaves during this stage of the process. The special fragrance and flavor of Phoenix Single Tree Oolong comes from correct indoor withering.

While the already-picked tea is undergoing indoor withering, I visit the high elevation tea garden. This day 250 pickers are working the mountain. They work very hard. The mountain is steep and rocky and the trails are few. One hundred year old tea trees dot the mountainside amid large volcanic rocks. They grow in the volcanic soil which provides the best nutrition for these tea trees.

The soil, clean mountain air, cold clear spring water, the view from the peak, excellent Tea Masters and extraordinary tea trees combine to create one of the finest teas in the world.

原生態的單欉茶園
Organic process is practiced for all tea varieties.

鳳凰山清晨
Phoenix Mountain in the early morning.

宋種單欉 - 800年樹齡
This is a Song Dynasty variety, 800 years old.

鳳凰單欉簡紀

Phoenix Single-Tree Oolong Tea

400年老單叢鮮葉
Fresh leaves from a 400 year old tree.

約900年前，鳳凰單欉起源於廣東省東北隅，潮汕鳳凰山區，風行於清朝(1644AD)年間，成為中國十大名茶已有百年歷史。如今在鳳凰高山地區，百年茶樹依然生機蓬勃，生產著獨特的茶香。

正宗的鳳凰單欉，有一套傳統而獨特的烏龍茶製作方式，部份生產技術、程序類似鐵觀音烏龍茶，但是在萎凋、發酵、焙火上略高略重，獨特之處是：老單欉樹形高大優美，單株即可有獨自的香形喉韻，即使是同一個老茶師，用同樣的生產程序技術，不同的老單欉依舊綻放自己的芬芳。

正宗的鳳凰單欉，僅生產於廣東省東北隅，潮汕鳳凰山區，此地海拔約1400公尺，高山、縱谷開闊深遠，地理環境優美，乃源自億萬年前的火山造山運動。高山上巨石林立，坡上覆蓋著深厚的有機質火山褐色土壤，山區終年雲霧環繞，濕度高、日夜溫差大，均為單欉創造了最佳生長環境。

鳳凰山區常年均溫18-22攝氏度，降雨量均衡穩定，高山單欉傍著巨石生長，百年以上茶樹、茶林隨處可見。100-400年老單欉大都是宋朝單欉的後代，800年前的單欉(宋種)依舊存活著，枝幹高大強健，枝葉覆蓋如傘，有二層樓高，大部份老單欉年均可生產10公斤單欉茶葉。

優質的鳳凰單欉每年春、秋兩季生產，採摘鮮葉時有三種情況不採收，高溫、高濕、雨霧天均不採，午時鮮葉採收以後，生產需不間斷地進行到半夜或更晚，才完成毛茶初制，鮮葉採收以後，是一連串細心的生產過程，首先是曬菁，接著是室內萎凋，室內萎凋對單欉製作非常重要，製茶師傅使用搖青、靜置來促進鮮葉發酵，浪菁、做菁也是室內萎凋過程中重要的環節，室內萎凋約需10-12小時才能完成。當鮮葉萎凋、發酵到一定的程度，製茶師傅需立下決定，進行殺菁(停止發酵)，殺菁後進行條揉、解條塊、初烘焙成毛茶。

毛茶完成數天后，製茶師傅再選擇同種類香型，質量一致的毛茶進行勻堆、揀梗、剔選，之後再進行4-6小時文火復焙。整個單欉的生產過程，複雜且精緻，每一位製茶師傅均需要10年以上的工作經驗，而我們的伙伴-製茶師傅都有20年以上的製作單欉經驗。

單欉毛茶生產完成需18-24小時，毛茶條索緊結修長，棕褐墨綠，帶霜色富有光澤，沖泡後葉面形成美麗的綠葉紅鑲邊，帶著優稚、強勁、濃馥幽長的密蘭香氣，茶湯入口，喉韻鮮爽、甘美有物，如啜佳釀。

鳳凰單欉始於900年前，風行於400年前的清朝，進而成中國十大名茶，在1986年鳳凰單欉取得中國烏龍茶比賽的金獎。現在鳳凰單欉已成為中國南方各省、南洋地區、台灣、上海等地茶迷的最愛之一。優良的鳳凰單欉在茗茶拍賣會上競價，每公斤價約在USD$1500-2000之間。

鳳凰單欉必需經過最後的文火复培才算完美，文火复培後的單欉，有令人難以置信的馥郁香氣，但是文火复培後最好存放兩週，使茶葉的火氣退除後再沖泡享用，最好的單欉香氣、韻味可能在一年後才表現出來，所以有些茶迷是一次買二斤，一斤立即享用，一斤存放到明年。鳳凰單欉不需存放在冷櫃或冰箱，但需選用密封性佳的茶缸，遠離高溫、光線直射，存放在涼爽、乾燥、通風、乾燥之處即可。

Phoenix Single-Tree Tea began 900 years in the past. It was first recognized as a top ten tea about 100 years ago. The Phoenix Single-Tree Oolong has been famous since the Qing Dynasty which began in 1644 A.D.. These long-living tea trees are still strong with the power to grow and provide rich energy, in the high mountains, even hundreds of years later. Single-Tree Oolong is produced in Guangdong province, China. Specifically in northeast Guangdong, near the city of Chaozhou.

Authentic Phoenix Single-Tree Oolong Tea is made using the traditional whole oolong tea process. This process is similar to what is use to produce the famous Tie Kuan Yin Oolong but the fermentation and the charcoal firing are both heavier. Phoenix Single-Tree Oolong Tea is particularly special because each wild plant produces its own fragrance. Each tree has a special, unique, and particular fragrance. Even when the same Tea Master uses the exact same process, each Phoenix Single-Tree Tea tree produces a difference fragrance.

Authentic Phoenix Single-Tree is produced only on Phoenix Mountain in the Chaozhou area. Millions of years ago, this mountain was a volcano. About 5,000 feet high, Phoenix Mountain is huge and stepped with deep crevasses between each layer of volcanic rock. It is always cloudy in the morning and the soil is very rich. Ever-cloudy with high humidity, and large temperature changes between day and night, Phoenix Mountain is perfect for producing an incredible and unique tea.

The average yearly temperature on Phoenix Mountain is about18- 22 degrees Celsius. Rainfall is regular, very even. The entire region is great for growing tea. In this rocky area with lots of big rocks, a large number of the tea trees are between 100 and 400 years old. They are only second or third generation removed from the original Song Dynasty plants. At least one 800 year old plant is still alive. Each tea plant is like a tree, as tall as a one- story building. Each tree produces about 20 pounds of tea each year.

The best Phoenix Single-Tree Oolong Tea is produced in the springtime and in the late fall. At harvest time, each picker must seriously judge the weather. If it is too sunny or it is too rainy or the humidity is too high…well, then the tea cannot be picked. If it is too foggy, no harvesting that day. This special tea is usually picked after 1pm. The entire process normally continues until midnight, or later.

Once picked, the tea must then be carefully processed. Outdoor withering is followed by indoor withering. Indoor withering is very important for Phoenix Single-Tree Oolong Tea. The Tea Master Must roll the tea leaf, let the leaf rest, and then let the tea go through indoor fermentation.

Dancing the leaf, shake the leaf, rest the leaf are part of indoor-withering, which takes about 10-12 hours total. When the Tea Master decides the fragrance is just the perfect strength, he must stop the fermentation immediately! Then he rolls the leaf, then separates the leaf. Next comes the first drying.

The tea rests for a few days then the Tea Master blends the tea in groups of the same quality and fragrance. Next comes charcoal firing, which takes 4-6 hours. Creation of Phoenix Single-Tree Oolong Tea is a complicated and delicate oolong tea process. Each Tea Master should have at least 10 years experience. Our TeaMaster Signature Tea group of Tea Masters average 20 years experience.

2009年4月27日當天有250位採茶人在鳳凰山頂採茶
Tea pickers working on Phoenix Mountain. This day is April 27, 2009.
About 250 tea pickers are working the mountain.

The entire process takes 18-24 hours. The finished tea is a beautiful straight-twist shape. The color is a lovely yellow and dark brown. The leaf is shiny. After brewing, the leaf opens. A beautiful red or gold halo surrounds the leaf edge. The center of the leaf is green.

The "Honey-orchid" fragrance of the TeaMaster Signature Phoenix Single-Tree Oolong Tea is incredible, powerful, yet not overwhelming, and long-lasting. This tea has a rich flavor. It lingers on the tongue like a fine wine: fresh, strong, and sweet.

This taste is unique to Phoenix Mountain. The tea began 900 years ago and became famous 400 years ago. In 1986 in China, at a famous tea competition, Phoenix Single-Tree Oolong Tea won first place, winning out over all other oolong teas.. Today, this tea is popular in south China, Hong Kong, Taiwan, and now even Shanghai.

茶園風光
Tea Garden

鳳凰山區
Phoenix Mountain.

烏凍-鳳凰山村
Oodong Village, a small village on Phoenix Mountain.

鳳凰山茶園
Phoenix Mountain tea garden

巨石岩旁的茶園
Tea plants grow amid large rocks.

岩石林立的茶園
Big rocks are scattered throughout the tea garden.

岩石、生態茶園、採茶人
The volcanic extrusions create natural steps which are then shaped by the tea workers.

海拔1300公尺的新茶園
Creating a new tea garden on the mountain top, 4200 feet.

火山岩石與棕壤
The unique properties of Phoenix Single-Tree are, in part, due to the volcanic soil.

有機質豐富的火山棕土壤
The volcanic soil is rich in nutrients.

登山採茶去
A picker climbs the mountain. This is fresh Phoenix tea leaf.

登山採茶去　　Pickers ascend the mountain.
樂在其中　　　A picker enjoys the work.
採茶之樂　　　Working with tea makes workers happy.

50~100年茶樹散佈在山頂岩石群中

Pickers work in the rock tea garden. These are 50-100 year old plants.

登山採茶去

Pickers climb the mountain single file. There is no defined path.

快樂的採茶人
A happy worker.

採茶人純樸的展示鮮葉
A peaceful honest worker shows off the tea leaves.

一棵小單欉，約10年樹齡

Picking leaves from a very young plant, about 10 years old.

鳳凰單欉鮮葉

Fresh Phoenix Single-Tree leaf.

鮮葉採摘方法之一
Demonstrating expert
picking technique.

鮮葉採摘方法之二
Leaf picking skill, the finger
is wrapped for protection.

鮮葉採摘方法之三
Workers develop fine
leaf picking skill.

① 快樂的鮮葉收集工
Happy leaf collector.

② 滿袋而歸
With a full bag of tea leaves, a worker heads for the truck.

③ 小貨車收集鮮葉送回茶廠
Fresh leaves are loaded into the truck.

④ 茶園管理者
The Supervisor of the tea garden.

宋種單欉根部 - 800年樹齡
The base of an 800 year old tea tree.

1

② ③

① 山頂上的清泉，冷洌甘甜。
A small waterfall near the top of Phoenix
Mountain. Spring water makes good tea and is sweet to drink.

② 800年宋種單欉與新生單欉
The same tree from a different side. The smaller plants are the younger generation.

③ 映山紅正開顏
Red "makes mountain beautiful flower" just opened.

400年老單欉
A 400 year old tea tree.

100年老單欉
A 100 year old tree variety.

平均200年老單欉茶林
Trees in this garden average 200 years old.

老單欉茶園
Old trees grow in a huge area.

宋種單欉繁殖的第三代茶園
Perhaps only the third generation removed from the original Song Dynasty trees.

100年老單欉翠綠強健
A 100 year old tree, so green and healthy.

① 成林老單欉茶園
　An old forest tea garden.

② 有機管理的單欉茶園
　An organic control tea garden.

③ 原生態的單欉茶園
　Semi-wild growing tea trees.

天池-海拔1400公尺的火山口湖
Palm of Heaven, a volcano crater, creates a small lake at the peak of Phoenix Mountain, with an elevation of 4500 feet.

火山岩石-海獅湖中靜臥
Volcanic rock in the middle of the lake,
sits like a sleeping sea lion.

火山岩上天池美
The beauty of Palm of Heaven.
Notice the Chinese characters on
volcanic rock…look close.

天池湖畔火山岩
A large volcanic rock at top of Phoenix
Mountain near Palm of Heaven Lake.

① 鳳凰山上小黃花 Low-growing high mountain yellow flowers.

② 特寫映山紅　A close up of the flower.

③ 映山紅映得滿山紅
　　A rare flowering plant grows among tea trees.
　　Its Chinese name is literally, "red color makes the mountain beautiful."

黃枝花-黃枝是中藥名,也是單欉十大香型名稱之一。
This "yellow bush" branch is used as Chinese medicine.
Yellow bush is the name of one kind of Phoenix Single-Tree Oolong flavor.

單欉幼苗
Leaves of a young Phoenix Single Tree Oolong tea plant.

單欉幼苗嫩葉
The leaf has opened on the young oolong tree.

單欉幼苗
Delicate leaves on a baby Phoenix Mountain oolong tree.

天池小茶莊位於鳳凰烏凍山頂-海拔1400公尺
The Palm of Heaven tea store at 5,000 feet on Phoenix Mountain.

① 鳳凰單欉大都午後開採鮮葉，寬邊草帽保護採茶人免於日曬，
這頂草帽是我在鳳凰山上的幸運帽。
A lucky number at Palm of Heaven. Phoenix Single Tree is picked after noon.
Tall-grass hats protect the workers from the hot high-mountain sun.

② 專注的採茶人
The shyest picker of all.

③ 鮮葉採摘方法之四
Expert picking technique, picker protection of arms is visible.

曬青 做青與
靜置萎凋

Withering and
Fermentation Withering

海拔1300公尺曬青場，午時單欉鮮葉，正在進行室外萎凋。
Phoenix Single-Tree leaves, outdoor withering at 5000 feet on Phoenix Mountain.

① 室外萎凋約30分鐘，製茶師傅們開始收集茶菁進入室內。
   After 30 minutes of outdoor withering, the tea leaves are collected by the
   Tea Master and brought indoors.

② 製茶師傅身著長袖上衣防寒，頭頂草帽防曬，進行室外萎凋。
   Another Tea Master separates leaves for outdoor withering. The strong sunlight
   requires a protective hat. The high mountain ultraviolet also requires
   long sleeves for protection.

③ 製茶師傅鋪曬茶菁，地面上覆膠布，確保茶菁不落地。
   A Tea Master separates the fresh leaves for outdoor withering.
   A plastic tarp protects the leaves and keeps them from touching the ground.

④ 鮮葉移入室內，堆起一定厚度，開始室內萎凋及發酵，單欉發酵程度約在40%～50%。
   Now begins the indoor withering. With a high-fermented tea like Phoenix Single Bush,
   40-50% fermentation, the fresh leaves are stacked thickly for indoor withering.

④

①

① 有30年經驗的製茶師傅正在舞動茶菁，促進茶菁自然碰撞，
有利於走水做菁，均衡發酵。
A Tea Master dances the leaves. This Tea Master has 30 years experience.
Dancing the leaves lightly bruises them, making indoor oxidizing easier.

② 室內萎凋及發酵。
Phoenix Single-Bush leaves, indoor withering.

③ 室內萎凋中檢視茶菁及做菁，均衡發酵。
A Tea Master inspects the leaves during indoor withering.

① 製茶師傅正在檢視茶菁及做菁。
A Tea Master rotates the leaves for indoor withering.
Properly preparing a top quality tea requires patience.

② 靜置堆放室內萎凋中茶菁逐漸發酵，顏色漸棕紅，體積漸縮小
During indoor withering the color of the leaves begins to change.
The leaves also become softer. The pile of leaves becomes smaller.

③ 搖菁之後，製茶師傅直接在大竹圓框裏舞動茶菁，促茶菁均衡發酵。
After tumbling, another Tea Master dances the leaves inside a big tumbler basket.

① 茶菁在搖菁之後也需靜置。
Now the leaves rest in the tumbler during indoor withering.

② 午後陽光輕灑與茶菁共映餘暉。
Late afternoon sun shines on beautiful leaves as fermentation continues.

③ 午後陽光輕灑，滿籠餘暉。
The afternoon light falls on the leaves.

④ 茶菁再堆厚靜置，發酵已進尾聲。
Thickly stacked again, the leaves are almost ready to stop fermentation.

⑤ 堆厚靜置，發酵已近完成。
The end of fermentation is near.

⑥ 茶菁覆蓋小睡片刻，提溫兼籠茶氣。
This is the final step in indoor withering. Then the fermentation stops.

⑦ 溫洵的午後餘暉，輕灑在最後階段發酵的茶菁上。
Gentle sunlight around 6pm for final indoor withering.
The leaves are warm but not too warm for slow final fermentation.

⑧ 小睡中的單欉茶菁。
Taking a peek at the "sleeping baby" Phoenix Single Tree Oolong leaves.

茶菁初現，清香悅人。
The fermented Phoenix Single Bush leaf.

殺青
停止發酵
Stop Fermentation

茶菁發酵完成，需即時殺菁-停止發酵。
It is time to stop fermentation.

① 茶菁完成發酵。
The fermentation is being stopped.

② 使用烘菁轉桶，桶底加熱進行殺菁。
Air firing to stop fermentation.

③ 傳統木料取火加熱。
Natural traditional fire work to heat stop-fermentation equipment.

④ 兩位製茶師傅親自升火，加熱烘菁機設備。
Two Tea Masters expertly adjust the temperature.

⑤ 兩位製茶師傅備茶菁而立，等待烘菁轉桶升溫， 溫度必需足夠才能停止茶菁再發酵。
Waiting for air firing equipment to reach correct temperature.
The temperature must be just right.

① 這位製茶師傅18歲開始學製茶，於今已有50年的經驗，他正向烘菁機投放茶菁。
This Tea Master has over 50 years of experience. After indoor withering,
he adds tea leaves for air firing to stop the fermentation.

② 殺青時需要非常專注速度及火候。
Stopping fermentation. The Tea Master must
be focused to do the job right.

③ 投放茶菁，進行殺青。
Air firing stops fermentation.

④ 茶菁在烘菁機內滾動。
Leaves tumble inside air firing equipment.

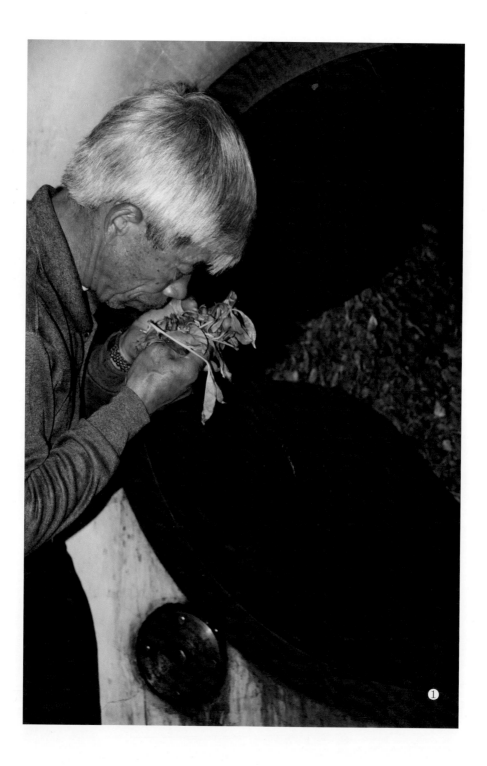

① 仔細審慎聞香
Judging the leaves.

② 重要時刻，仔細聞香以正確判斷火候是否如夠，判斷錯誤，
茶菁將不熟而帶菁味，或者過熟變成焦味。
An important time. Smell the leaves. Is it time to stop air firing?
Get it wrong and the tea is either too smoky or too fresh.

③ 判斷殺青的時間，何時起鍋非常重要，廠長與負責人都親自參與。
Stop firing is so important the Owner and the General Manager both judge the leaf.

檢視正在倒出的茶菁。
A Tea Master inspects the leaves at the end of air firing.

① 殺菁到位，茶菁必需即時起鍋倒出， 過程約10秒。

The air fire process is finished. The leaves must be removed within ten seconds.

② 茶菁快速的倒出，承接移動需快手快腳。

End of air firing, remove the leaves quickly.

③ 左邊的茶菁已完成殺菁， 右邊的茶菁正要開始殺菁。

Leaves on the left are at the end of air firing. The leaves on the right are just beginning to be air fired.

④ 解散剛倒出的茶菁，利於快速降溫。

At the end of air firing, the hot leaves are separated to cool them.

條揉與
解索條
Rolling

茶菁殺菁之後，立即進行條揉。
Rolling the Phoenix Single Bush leaf after "stop fermentation."

① 準備條揉機，投放已停止發酵的菁葉。
A Tea Master puts tea leaves in the rolling machine, adding a little pressure.

② 兩位製茶師傅，一位忙著為菁葉加壓，一位忙著清理菁葉。
Rolling process, one Tea Master adds pressure while another cleans the leaf.

③ 茶菁通過條揉後，已成條索形狀。
The tea leaves emerge from the rolling machine.

④ 30年經驗的製茶師傅，正在準備解開塊狀索條。
Another Tea Master with 30 years experience moves rolled tea to the separator.

⑤ 投放塊狀索條，進行解索。
A Tea Master places tea leaves in the separator.

⑥ 索條茶菁，均勻地在竹編圓框上，等待初次烘焙。
Leaving the separator, the tea leaves are now more separate and even, ready for the first drying.

條揉之後的菁葉，帶著棕紅茶梗，水色鮮活。
After rolling, moisture comes out of the leaf and the stem turns red.

等待初烘焙的茶菁，鮮活潤澤。
Before the first drying, the leaf brims with life.

茶菁己上架，分層排列等待初焙。
Leaves are arranged and stacked for the first drying.

茶菁帶著綠葉鑲紅邊，色澤明亮等待初焙。
Shiny brown and green leaves await the first drying.

初烘 焙

審視茶質

First Drying and Tea Tasting

傳統式柴火烘焙爐。
Preparing the equipment for first drying. It is heated with a wood fire.

1

②

① 120攝氏度即可開始烘焙茶菁。
The correct temperature for
drying is 120 degrees Celsius.

② 午夜時分，烘焙室裏正忙碌
烘焙茶菁。
Near midnight the tea leaves
are loaded into the drying
equipment.

③ 茶菁移往最上層烘焙。
Tea in a bamboo basket is
loaded into the upper level
of the dryer.

④ 疲憊的茶師猶不鬆懈地檢查
焙好的毛茶。
A tired Tea Master tests the
temperature of the cooling
leaves.

⑤ 經過一天的勞動，午夜時分
烘焙室裏再持續工作，是體
能的考驗。
A long day continues as the
tea is removed from the dryer.

⑥ 檢視毛茶。
A Tea Master separates the
dried leaves.

③   ④

⑤

⑥

初焙完成，毛茶在已泛棕紅色的竹架上退溫，此時單欉已完成80%的製作，每位製茶師傅都迫不及待的想嚐試茶湯內質。

At the end of first drying the tea cools. The bamboo trays have changed color from the heat. Now the tea is about 80% finished. After a long day of work everyone is eager to taste it.

這是豐收的時刻，單欉毛茶正在冷却中，退溫之後即可審評內質。
It is harvest time. The tea dries and cools, waiting to be tasted.

單欉毛茶
A close look at the finished first-dry leaves. This is called Original Dry.

①　②

① 流暢、美感十足的功夫茶道
Exceptional pouring skill, perfectly brewed tea, perfect color.

② 令人興奮的時刻，茶師傅正在使用蓋碗審評單欉毛茶，小蓋碗約180cc，置茶量10～12克，毛茶几乎裝滿蓋碗，衝入沸水後.首先要審聞香氣，香氣是啜飲單欉重要的一環；茶湯滋味當然也很重要，回甘喉韻不可忽視，湯色金黃明亮，玉帶環杯更不可錯過，至於葉底當然是綠葉鑲紅邊。
An exciting time. The Tea Master brews the new Original tea leaves in a traditional Gaiwan. Boiling water is poured onto 10-12 grams of tea leaves. The first taste checks fragrance which is a very important quality of Phoenix Single Tree. Of course, taste is always important, checking for sweetness and lingering. Tea color is important, too. It should be a lovely gold. Finally, inspect the tea leaves after brewing. The leaf must be green inside and golden brown around the edges.

③ 使用蓋碗審評單欉毛茶。
Brewing the Original new tea in the Gaiwan.

④ 蓋碗、飲杯、潮式功夫茶道。
High skill, here, using a Gaiwan to pour the tea Gongfu style. The Tea Master controls the Gaiwan perfectly.

⑤ 潛心靜氣品單欉，空山明月有清風。
Completely relaxed, with extreme and perfect concentration, the Tea Master enjoys the fruits of his labor.

單欉毛茶，毫芒初顯。

First dry, Original tea leaves fill the Gaiwan, waiting for the boiling water to release fragrance and flavor.

千錘百煉草中英，浴火重生返復來。

After the first infusion, the Black Dragon awakens to share the incredible fragrance and flavor. The leaves are coming back to life.

紫玉入翠色，岩骨又花香。

After 3 or 4 steepings, the invigorated tea leaves show rich colors of green, brown, purple, orange, and yellow.

身披翠色衣，內蘊奇岩香。

Phoenix Single-Tree after one steeping. A different variety produces different colors.

金枝玉葉藏不住，初顯風華上雲天。

After 3 or 4 steepings the leaves are more open as they hydrate.

白瓷托素心，翠色滿山園。

Beautiful leaves fill the Gaiwan.

鳳凰茶友

The Tea Master from Phoenix Mountain

天池茶業 鄭協龍先生

Palm of Heaven Tea Company Vice President.

鳳凰山上採茶女
A lovely young woman picking the tea on Phoenix Mountain

① 50年製茶經驗的製茶師。
50-years-experience Tea Master.

② 哥倆好-兄弟檔製茶師。
Two brothers: one old and one young.

③ 天池茶廠廠長。
Palm of Heaven Tea Company Manufacturing Director.

④ 父與子-父子檔製茶師。
Father and son.

⑤ 天池茶業 柯江明先生。
Palm of Heaven Tea Company Owner.

⑥ 含蓄的姑娘-忙著準備試茶用的熱水。
A shy and lovely young woman prepares the hot water for tasting.

⑦ 茶園守護者。
The Tea Garden Supervisor, he guards the garden.

⑧ 茶廠技術領班。
Manufacturing Supervisor.

⑨ 茶菁萎凋室領班。
Indoor Withering Supervisor.

茶山紀行

鳳凰單欉

A Tea-Lover's Travel Diary

Phoenix · Single-Tree

2009年4月27日我前往鳳凰山訪茶，一路茶香伴攝影，收穫頗豐，不虛此行，藉此小集一隅，特向鳳凰山上諸茶友，表示衷心的感謝！更向保持傳統鳳凰製茶工藝的師傅們致最高的敬意。

April 4, 2009, I went to Phoenix Mountain. My sole purpose was the study of Phoenix Single-Tree Oolong Tea. Travel is always educational. In this case, it increased my knowledge of a very special tea. The people in this tea garden work very hard to maintain the valuable tradition of authentic Phoenix Single Tree Oolong Tea. To all of them, everyone, I say, "Thank you."

鳳凰單樅製作工序一覽
Phoenix Single-Tree Oolong Tea:The Process

採 茶
Tea plucking

曬青(日光萎凋)
Outdoor Withering (Sunshine Withering)

做青(室內萎凋)
Indoor Withering

殺青(停止發酵)
Stop fermentation

條 揉
Rolling

解索塊
Separating the Leaves

初烘焙
First dry

審視茶質
Tasting the Tea

二週後篩選精製
Two weeks later sorting the leaves
Selecting the Best

炭火低溫複烘焙
The Final Fire Charcoal Drying

茶品檢測
Quality inspection and Tea cupping

成品包裝
Product packaging

鳳凰單欉沖泡方法

沖泡鳳凰單欉，以紫砂小壺、功夫茶具為上選，並採用山泉好水，滾水備用，先溫壺後置入約半壺的茶量，再沖水入壺一半，隨即倒出，既用于醒茶，也用于享用單欉獨特的香氣；第二次沖入滾水滿壺，靜置約30秒即可倒出在小杯飲用，單欉使用功夫茶具沖泡，通常可以沖泡20次以上。

一般茶壺沖泡，約1克茶葉配合60cc的滾水，600cc的茶壺配用10克茶葉，浸泡3～4分鐘後飲用，一般可以沖泡3～5次。

茶師傅自動沖茶杯，置茶量6～7克，選用好水煮沸加入即可，約三分鐘即沖泡完成，一般可以沖泡5～7次。

The Perfect Cup of Phoenix Single-Tree Oolong

The traditional way to enjoy this tea is Gongfu style (Kungfu).

Use a small Yixing clay teapot and fill the teapot halfway with the tea leaf. Always begin with good boiling water.

During the first steep, in the teapot, rinse the leaf with a small amount of boiling water and let it sit on the leaves for 10 seconds. Pour the water off. Then enjoy the fragrance of the leaves. This is often called "Awakening the Dragon." Always use boiling water 205-210F for this tea. For the second steeping, add the water, then pour the tea after 30 seconds steep time. Serve in small tea cups.

Phoenix Single-Tree Oolong Tea can be steeped up to 20 times when using the Gongfu method. The tea always has a similar flavor but the aroma changes with each steeping, so please enjoy the fragrance change.

When brewing with a normal tea pot, use one gram dry leaf, for every 2 ounces of water. For a 20 ounce tea pot use ten grams tea. Steep 3-4 minutes. Enjoy 3-5 times.

For the TeaMaster Automatic Tea Brewer® use 6-7 grams of tea. Add boiling water. In about three minutes your tea will be ready. Enjoy 5-7 times.

鐵觀音

Tie Kuan Yin Oolong Tea

鐵觀音之間記

"鐵觀音"原產中國、福建安溪，屬烏龍名種，半發酵茶類，主要產茶區海拔1000米，羣山環抱，峰巒疊翠，晨昏夕陰，山嵐雲霧，四時滋潤，紅壤土質，呈弱酸性，山華地靈，非常適宜茶的生長。

鐵觀音是中國十大名茶之一，清雍正年間發現創制。茶區境內野生茶樹散布，其中藍田山區發現的千年茶樹，樹高7米，如傘覆蓋，生機昂然，足証安溪茶區歷史悠久。

安溪縣志記載，鐵觀音起源于西坪松岩村，魏蔭所發現培育，時名-魏蔭種。相傳約1723年，堯陽松岩村茶農魏蔭（1703-1775）勤農務茶，誠信佛教，每日晨昏敬奉觀世音菩薩像前一杯清茶，十年如一日。有一天睡夢中，携鋤出門，行至溪澗旁邊，在石縫中發現一株茶樹，枝強葉茂，異香宜人，與生平所見的茶樹均不同。清晨醒來立即順着夢中情景尋找，果然在溪澗石崖旁，找到夢中的茶樹，小茶樹紫紅嫩芽，葉肉肥厚，碧綠青翠，他滿懷欣喜小心取下鮮葉，返家立即依烏龍茶之法作茗茶，沖泡後花香高雅，如蘭似桂，茶湯入口鮮爽甘甜。舌底生津，回味無窮確是名種奇茗，立夏即返回母樹進行壓苗育植，隔年春再移新枝苗種在家中鐵鼎裏，悉心培育分諸親友，因感念觀音托夢所得，故取名"鐵觀音"。

時安溪堯陽人　王仕讓任職朝廷副貢，乾隆六年奉召進京，謁禮部侍郎方苞,以魏蔭種烏龍茶為禮品，方侍郎品啜後知其非凡，轉進皇室內庭，乾隆皇帝喜其色、香、味、形均美，讚譽有加，因其身骨沉重，烏潤似鐵，遂賜名："鐵觀音"。

鐵觀音是中等發酵（40%）的烏龍茶，製茶工藝繁多，複雜且嚴懂。採茶依全年節氣，分春、夏、暑、秋四季採收，品質以春、秋茶最佳，春茶味厚，秋茶香高，各領千秋，夏暑茶則次之。採茶依日時，則分早菁、午菁、晚菁三種，其中以日照充足的午菁最佳，採摘鮮葉有五不原則—不折斷鮮葉、不折疊葉脈、不碰碎葉尖、不採單葉及老梗。

新鮮完整的鮮葉採回，立即進行曬青、攤菁靜置、搖青(做青)，也就是日光萎凋、室內萎凋的發酵工藝；鮮葉攤菁由薄攤到厚攤，時間由短到長；鮮葉搖菁由慢到快，手法由輕到重，傳統做法需搖菁四～五次，俗諺：一搖勻，二搖水，三搖香，四搖紅，五搖看天時。直到走水完足，菁氣除盡轉為馥郁，綠葉紅邊，茶菁發酵達40%，需即時炒青、殺青，停止鮮葉發酵，以確保香氣、滋味完美的呈現；過程約18～24小時。

殺青之後是一連串的揉捻工序，團揉及解塊需反覆進行20次以上，待到鮮葉形成卷曲緊結外形，再進行初焙完成毛茶制作；毛茶揀梗之後再篩分、風選、揀剔、勻堆成品後再複焙，複焙需用文火低溫，使毛茶中的水份與咖啡鹼緩慢蒸發，在乾茶外形成一層淡霜，俗稱起霜才算完成鐵觀音茶的製作。精心焙制後的鐵觀音外形卷曲緊結，條索厚實勻淨，略呈螺旋狀，茶骨沈重，色澤青綠微霜。

十八世紀清代中期，中國南方一帶就盛行品嚐鐵觀音，特別在漳卅、泉卅、廈門家家皆飲，戶戶均藏，成為生活上的必需品。如今則是中國南方各省，家中最佳待客之道，並且風行亞州，揚名歐美，品茗競誇鐵觀音，成為中國茗茶另一個代名詞。

沖泡"鐵觀音"講究使用小巧精緻的紫砂茶壺、或是白瓷蓋碗茶杯，精選水質即燒、即沖、即飲，趁熱聞香品茗，上品鐵觀音茶湯金黃明亮，香氣馥郁悠長，滋味鮮爽，喉韻醇厚、甘美，齒頰留香，如空谷幽蘭,令人回味無窮。 譽之： 美如觀音重似鐵，七品太和猶餘香。

優質鐵觀音可從"觀形、聽聲、審色、葉底、聞香、品韻"辨別判斷。

觀形：色澤青綠微霜，卷曲緊結，厚實勻淨。
聽聲：茶身緊結，茶骨沈重，置茶入壺，清脆作響。
審色：傳統清香型—湯色金黃帶綠，光灩清澈。
　　　炭焙濃香型—湯色金黃澄亮，光灩清澈。
葉底：葉底厚實明亮,葉背外曲，
　　　光澤似紙似綢，手揉不爛。
聞香：傳統清香型—蘭香優雅、馥郁悠長。
　　　炭焙濃香型—異香撲鼻、滿室芬芳。
品韻：品啜甘美，舌底生津，滋味鮮爽，喉韻醇厚。

■ 使用一般茶壺沖泡，約600cc的茶壺配用7-8克茶葉，浸泡3～5分鐘後飲用，一般可以沖泡2-3次。

■ 使用茶師傅自動沖茶杯，置茶量7克，選用好水煮沸加入即可，約三分鐘即沖泡完成。

■ 鐵觀音需收貯在密封性佳的茶罐，遠離高溫、光線直射，存放在涼爽、乾燥、通風、乾燥之處。長期貯藏以冷櫃或冰箱最佳，可長期保鮮。

About Tie Kuan Yin

Authentic and traditional Tie Kuan Yin is produced in Fujian province, in the Anxi area, in China. Tie Kuan Yin, also called Iron Goddess of Compassion, is one of the most famous oolong teas. It is grown in the mountains at about 3,000 feet. There are many mountains in the Anxi area, peak after peak. It is a beautiful landscape. Afternoons in these mountains are almost always cloudy. There is good moisture in all four seasons. The land is red and rich in iron. The soil tests slightly acidic or sour. The mountains are majestic, the land is elegant. It is perfect for tea growing.

Tie Kuan Yin is one of the top ten most famous Chinese teas. It was created early in the Qing Dynasty. The area in Fujian where it began has many wild-growing tea trees. One of these trees is about 1,000 years old and over 20 feet in height. The old tree still produces good leaves. The very age of this tree indicates the long history of tea in Anxi.

The Anxi area has its own written record of Tie Kuan Yin varieties. Tie Kuan Yin began in Xipin county in the village of Song Yan Cun. The founder of Tie Kuan Yin was Wei Yin. In fact, this tea was originally called "Wei Yin" variety. The ancient story says Mr. Wei Yin (1703-1775 C.E.) was a tea farmer. He worked very hard.

He was also a good Buddhist. Every morning before he began work, he would offer a cup of tea to the goddess, Kuan Yin Pu Sa. For ten years he did this every day, unfailingly. Then one night in 1723, Wei Yin had a dream. In this dream, he went to the village. There he saw the large stream that ran nearby. Growing next to the stream beside a large rock, Wei Yin discovered a very unusual tea variety. This tea was strong, with a unique fragrance. It was indeed special, and different. Upon awaking, Wei Yin followed his dream to the village. There he found the tea variety just where it had been in his dream. This tea plant had small purple and red buds. The leaves were thick, dark green, and shiny. Happy that his dream had literally come true, Wei Yin picked some tea leaves. At home he used the oolong process to make tea. When it was finished and brewed, Wei Yin tested the tea. It was a tea of the highest order with fragrances of orchid and osmanthus. He drank the

tea and it was sweet and lingering under the tongue. It was then that Wei Yin knew he had discovered an extraordinary tea variety. That same year, in late spring or early summer, he went back to the mother-tree to make new plants from cuttings. The following year, in the spring, Wei Yin moved the new variety, replanting it on his farm. There was an old iron pan that been used for pan firing. It now had a hole in the bottom and it was perfect protection for nurturing young plants. Wei Yin shared this new variety with his family and friends.

Tie Kuan Yin became famous for two reasons. First: Wei Yin and his discovery of the cultivar. Second: A gentleman, Mr. Wang Shi Rang, worked for the Qing Dynasty government. In 1742, the 6th year of the reign of Emperor Qianlong, Mr. Wang went to Beijing bringing some Wei Yin tea with him. This tea was a special gift to Emperor Qianlong. The Emperor was a tea connoisseur and he immediately fell in love with the new tea. Qianlong declared the virtues of this tea as rich in color, special in fragrance, sweet and lingering, and having an imposing presence like iron. He gave it a new name: Tie Kuan Yin.

Tie Kuan Yin is 40% oxidized tea. The processing is complicated, delicate and serious. Tie Kuan Yin is harvested four times a year: Spring, early Summer, later Summer, and Fall. Rating the quality: Spring is best, it is the sweetest and richest; the Fall product is very fragrant; early and late Summer are not as good as the first two. The fresh leaves are picked at three different times: early morning, noon, and late afternoon. For Tie Kuan Yin, noon-picked is the best. There are five rules when picking fresh leaf: 1. Do not break the leaf. 2. Do not crease the leaf. 3. Keep the leaf whole, especially the bud. 4. Always pick one bud two leaves for oolong style. 5. Do not pick old leaves.

After picking the fresh leaves, the sunshine withering must be done immediately. Then proceed to indoor withering. During indoor withering, the fresh leaves are stacked thinly at the beginning. The stacks become thicker, more dense, with subsequent witherings. Withering time also increases with each repetition of the process. When tumbling the leaves in the basket, start slow, too. Then increase speed with each tumbling. For traditional indoor withering, rolling in the bamboo tumblers should be done 4-5 times. 1. The first rolling makes the moisture in the leaves even. 2. This rolling lets the moisture come out. 3. This rolling creates the fragrance. 4. This sometimes-final rolling creates the red ring around the edge of the leaf. 5. This optional rolling is at the discretion of the Tea Master and usually takes place if the weather is cloudy or rainy. When the leaf has a beautiful fragrance and the green leaf has a red rim, it is time to stop indoor withering. The entire process takes about 18-24 hours.

After Stop Fermentation, the rolling continues. The leaves must be rolled (compressed) and separated for more than 20 times until they have the beautiful and traditional twist to their shape and the ball is properly compressed. Then it is time for the first drying. At this stage the tea is often called "Mao Cha." The Mao Cha has many stems which need to be removed by hand. After the stems are removed comes the second drying which is traditionally done with a charcoal fire. The charcoal fire must be at a low temperature and takes 4-8 hours. During this firing the moisture comes out of the leaf and the now-dry leaf will have a very, very light patina of white powder, looking for all-the-world like light snow or frost in the early morning. This ends the Tie Kuan Yin process, only save the final heavy twisting. Now the color is dark green with a hint of snow.

In the middle of the 18th century, during the Qing Dynasty in south China, Tie Kuan Yin became very popular, especially in some cities: Zhangzhou, Quanzhou, Xiamen. Then, most families would drink Tie Kuan Yin and always keep some at home. It became a lifestyle. Historically, Tie Kuan Yin became synonymous with China Tea. Today, Tie Kuan Yin is still very popular in southern China, also throughout Asia, Europe, and in the United States.

The preferred brewing method for Tie Kuan Yin is with the small unglazed clay Yixing teapot, or with a white porcelain gaiwan. Good water is very important. As soon as the water comes to a boil, brew the tea. Do not wait. Now, enjoy the fragrance while the tea is hot. Next, drink the tea from a small cup, enjoying the lingering flavor and the fragrance.

The best Tie Kuan Yin, brewed, has a beautiful and bright golden color. The fragrance is incredible and is far-reaching, seeming to fill a room. Drinking the tea, the flavor is clean and sweet with wonderful lingering. After drinking a cup of Tie Kuan Yin, the entire mouth is suffused with the fragrance. Like the fragrance of a mountain orchid, once you smell the aroma of Tie Kuan Yin, you will never forget it.

A popular tea poem recited by tea lovers: The tea is beautiful like Kuan Yin Pu Sa, but heavy like iron. (Meaning the dry tea is heavy in the hand in the sense of something of substance.).

After seven cups your mind feels peaceful and the tea still has fragrance. There are six ways to judge the best Tie Kuan Yin. 1. Shape. 2. Sound. 3. Color. 4. Leaf after brewing. 5. Fragrance. 6. Taste.

Appearance: Look at the dry leaf. It should have beautiful green and dark green colors with a hint of snow. The shape is tight with a twist. The outside is pure and even. Sound: Drop the dry tea on a table or on porcelain. A good Tie Kuan Yin tinkles like tiny bells. Color when brewed: Traditional Tie Kuan Yin is light golden-yellow and green with much brightness, high reflectance. When charcoal fired it is golden-yellow with orange having high light reflectance, bright. Leaf after brewing: The leaf is thick and curled inward, convex. The leaf is shiny and difficult to break. Fragrance: Traditional style has an orchid fragrance. Charcoal fire has a very special, different fragrance, sometimes like a flower, it fills the room and makes your nose comfortable. Taste: Sweet, beautiful, under the tongue is moist; smooth, not astringent, and beautiful lingering.

When using a normal teapot heat 600 cc water (about 20 oz) using 7-8 gm of dry leaf and steep 3-5 minutes. The same measure of tea may be steeped 2-3 times.

With the TeaMaster Automatic Tea Brewer: use 7 gm dry leaf, add boiling water. In about 3 minutes the tea will be finished and ready to drink. This is good for 2-3 steepings.

Tie Kuan Yin must be stored in a tight tea canister in a cool and dry place. For long-time storage the refrigerator is best.

茶園風光

Tea Garden

中國 福建 安溪茶都

春茶季節，破曉時分，茶農滙集，人聲鼎沸，當季新焙毛茶，茶香四溢，市集內賣茶、買茶、試菜、鬥茶，各有知音，熱鬧非凡，是世界上最繁忙的鐵觀音烏龍茶集散地。

The largest Tie Kuan Yin shopping mall in the world. It is always busy, but especially during the spring harvest time. Every day the farmers bring in fresh Tie Kuan Yin for customers. From the early morning the whole market is busy with tea tasting and selling tea. Tea lovers avidly search for the best.

2009年10月13日安溪茶都即景之一
Anxi Tea Market, October 13, 2009, buyers evaluating tea for wholesale.

安溪茶都即景之二
October 13, 2009 A busy day of tea buying at Anxi Market.

安溪茶都之三
The same day in Anxi Market, customers wait to purchase Tie Kuan Yin.

安溪茶都之四
Buyers in the Anxi Market checking the quality of Tie Kuan Yin on the same day.

清 王公士讓之像 —— 鐵觀音茶的開拓者之一
One of the founders of Tie Kuan Yin, during the Qing Dynasty, 300 years ago.

福建 安溪縣 西坪南陽山麓，鐵觀音茶的發源地之一。
Anxi Xipin village, South Mountain, the birthplace of Tie Kuan Yin oolong tea.

南陽鐵觀音, 依旁著巨石向陽之地生機昂然。
The original Tie Kuan Yin varietal plant still flourishes in the same area.

南陽鐵觀音嫩葉
Tie Kuan Yin leaves.

南陽鐵觀音
The Tie Kuan Yin original varietal plant. The birthplace of Tie Kuan Yin.

福建安溪清水古寺，八百年前創建，即種植茶樹。
Anxi Buddhist temple, 800 years old.

清水寺聖泉
Pure spring water for good tea at Qin Shui Buddhist temple.

清水寺 觀世音菩薩 石像
Kuan Yin Pu Sa, a stone version of the Lady stands in her own garden.

老松如伞，一枝獨秀。
Like an umbrella, this old pine tree stands over the tea garden.

梯田式茶園
Workers picking the tea in a stepped garden.

背山向陽，山勢斜緩，排水良好，雲露圍繞著紅土壤，這就是感德著名的高山茶園，
也是感德鐵觀音成為後起之秀的主因。
Red earth, gentle slopes, and the yang side of the mountain
in the sun produces superior Tie Kuan Yin.

山區茶園以5-15年的鐵觀音茶樹為主，鮮葉內質亦佳。
The plants in this tea garden are 5-15 years old.
They benefit from the nutrient-rich soil of the mountain.

鐵觀音茶樹，少見老欉，景緻因此雄壯開闊，平遠秀麗。
This panoramic tea garden grows the preferred young tea plants.
No large old plants obscure the view.

感德高山茶園海拔1400公尺，茶種－紅心歪尾挑，茶樹齡－約5-20年。
Gande Tea Garden at 5200 feet in Anxi Mountain.
This is the authentic and traditional Red Heart Peach variety of Tie Kuan Yin. On this mountain most plants are about 5-20 years old.

紅壤土的高山茶園
Tie Kuan Yin grows best in the light-red earth of the center peak.

感德山區蘊藏鐵礦，採礦聚合形成山村。
A village of iron. Iron is mined and processed in these mountains. The ferrous-red earth gives a different meaning to Tie Kuan Yin, Iron Goddess of Compassion.
An ancient traditional village house sits amidst old Tie Kuan Yin plants.

海拔800公尺的平台茶園，面積約200畝。

The other side of the Anxi mountains, at 2,400 feet, where a hard-working farmer leveled the top of one hill to grow more Tie Kuan Yin in the good red earth, 200 mu ("Mu" can mean "field," also 1/15 of a hectare.) of quality tea.

2009年4月30日，感德海拔1000公尺茶區，懸崖邊上採茶女。
The best tea grows in the 3300 feet mountains. Pickers must work carefully to harvest fresh Tie Kuan Yin leaves.

安溪 感德 - 鐵觀音茶苗。
Baby Tie Kuan Yin plants in front of a traditional house.

安溪 感德，鐵觀音茶苗園。
Baby Tie Kuan Yin plants ready to be sold off for cultivation in other parts of China, although most of these plants will remain in Fujian province.

山區氣溫涼爽，日照紫外線強，採茶需防寒、防曬。
Picking the good Tie Kuan Yin leaf, a picker needs protection against cool weather and strong sun. Both are ideal ingredients for growing fine tea.

① 鐵觀音樹齡不高，形矮而橫生，採茶需低腰彎身。
Harvesters bow to pick the Tie Kuan Yin variety, which grows to a medium height.

② 採茶話桑麻。
Tea workers put fresh leaves in a traditional bamboo basket. The workers chat as they pick, talking about family and friends and village life.

③ 剪法採茶適合面積大，密集橫生的茶園。
Some leaves are harvested with thumb and finger, but for larger areas workers may use modern scissors.

① 鐵觀音鮮葉
Fresh Tie Kuan Yin leaves, just picked.

② 鐵觀音鮮葉— 3~5年茶樹的鮮葉，最受市場歡迎。
Fresh leaves from 3-5 year-old plant. The most popular age for leaves in the Tie Kuan Yin market.

③ 採茶歸來
A tea picker just returned from the mountain with fresh Tie Kuan Yin leaves.

④ 2009年4月30日午時，日照正好，最宜茶菁日光萎凋。
April 30, 2009, high noon. Picking of the finest leaves ends at noon, the perfect time to begin sunshine withering.

鐵觀音正欉-紅心歪尾桃之茶芽
Red Heart Peach variety young leaf.

剛舒展的鐵觀音茶芽
The young bud, a baby leaf just open for the Red Heart Peach variety of Tie Kuan Yin.

鐵觀音茶芽-嫩葉泛著綠紫黃
Close-up the same baby bud.

安溪山產 – 批把
Delicious pippa fruit, a traditional Chinese delicacy.

山上的向日葵
Mountain sunflower.

① 山上的仙人掌花
Desert flower growing in Anxi mountains, as big as a tree.

② 安溪山區梔子花，五月盛開，芬芳清遠，與鐵觀音茶產期相同，各湧奇香，識者用以薰製茶葉。
Gardenia flowers bloom in May. They are often used to scent fine Chinese tea including green Tie Kuan Yin.

③ 梔子花
Night approaches and highlights young gardenia buds, not yet open.

西坪. 堯陽茶區 – 安溪鐵觀音原產地
Xipin county, Yao Yang Mountain. "Forest Peak" is the birthplace of Tie Kuan Yin, 1723 C.E.. The Tie Kuan Yin varietal originated on this mountain. This is one of the majestic views on the way to see the original Tie Kuan Yin.

堯陽茶區

A Yao Yang Mountain Red Peach Tie Kuan Yin tea garden. All of
these plants are children of the original varietal.

堯陽茶區
Tie Kuan Yin growing on one of the Yao Yang peaks.

堯陽山村
The beautiful houses of Yao Yang village. Authentic and traditional Tie Kuan Yin brings the prosperity of the Goddess.

① 茶山村落
Yao Yang village viewed from the other side.

② 西坪茶山
Another beautiful Yao Yang peak rich with Iron Goddess of Compassion tea plants.

欉生鐵觀音茶樹

Red Peach Tie Kuan Yin grows over a rock wall in the village. These plants have received special care.

西坪 松林頭，海拔約900公尺— 鐵觀音原產地
At 2,700 feet on Pine Forest Peak, the Tie Kuan Yin is well-manicured.

西坪 松林頭 打石坑茶山
Da Su Kun valley. The mountain spring flowing down makes a distinctive sound as of a
"fist hitting the stone."

松林頭 打石坑，鐵觀音原生母樹，西元1723年發現，迄今樹齡286年。
In 1723 C.E. the mother-tree was found on Pine Forest Peak, Da Su Kun valley. This tea tree is 283 years old. It is cut every year creating a short tree with a huge base. Here is the beginning of Tie Kuan Yin Oolong.

松林頭，打石坑，鐵觀音母樹傍山、依石、臨澗，坐東向西，生長環境優越獨特。

Why is mother-tree Tie Kuan Yin so special？ In this long view the Da Su Kun spring flows down the rocks from the north. Behind the mother-tree a large rock shields the tree from the eastern sun, and it receives the sun from the west.

西坪 松林頭 打石坑
In Da Su Kun valley, a statue of Kuan Yin Pu Sa stands just above, guarding the mother-tree. Pickers harvest the fine tea, a product of the best sun and water.

松林頭打石坑，鐵觀音母樹欉。
A stone marker commemorates the mother-tree.

西元1723年，茶農魏蔭，依夢中觀世音菩薩所示，發現鐵觀音母樹。
安溪縣志記載，鐵觀音起源于西坪松岩村，魏蔭所發現培育，時名-魏蔭種。
Wei Yin, the tea farmer who discovered the mother-tree is remembered in this stone
monument which sits between Kuan Yin Pu Sa's statue and the original plant.

打石坑鐵觀音母樹上之嫩芽
A young Red Peach leaf on the mother-tree.

打石坑鐵觀音母樹上之嫩葉。
正宗品種為紅心歪尾桃，以新芽帶紅，葉尖斜形似桃得名。
The best part for Tie Kuan Yin oolong, one bud three leaves.
The traditional and authentic Tie Kuan Yin variety is called Red Heart Peach because the center bud is red and shaped like a heart, and the leaf is shaped like a peach.

打石坑鐵觀音母樹上之嫩葉
A bud on the mother-tree. The leaves of the wild tea tree are strong and enduring.

① 打石坑，因澗水入石坑，如溪石相撞有聲得名。

The beautiful spring water of Da Su Kun strikes the stone making its distinctive sound.

② 打石坑鐵觀音母樹根部。

Multiple trunks support and sustain the mother-tree.

③ 打石坑鐵觀音母樹上之老葉。

Older leaves on the mother-tree.

百年鐵觀音茶樹根部。

A young Red Peach Tie Kuan Yin tree trunk. This tree is a mere 100 years old.

2009年10月12日，安溪 西坪 採秋茶
August 12, 2009, farmers harvest Red Peach Tie Kuan Yin. Their clothing protects them in the mountains.

西坪採茶
Autumn harvest August 12, 2009 in Xipin Yao Yang.

鐵觀音茶樹 性喜微酸性砂質紅壤
Tie Kuan Yin trees love iron-rich soil, slightly red and slightly sour.

微酸性紅壤
Red soil is best for growing Tie Kuan Yin. Iron Goddess loves iron-rich soil.

Sunshine withering
and Indoor withering

茶菁重幾許?
Two generations team up to weigh the fresh Tie Kuan Yin leaves.

攤菁、曬菁
Moisture must be removed from the tea leaves during processing. This begins with
a very important step, outdoor or sunshine withering.

日光萎凋之一，海拔800公尺曬菁場
This tea garden stands at 2,400 feet. Workers spread the leaves evenly for proper sunshine withering.

日光萎凋之二
The mountain sun removes moisture from the fresh leaves.

① 日光萎凋
A worker, protected from the harsh mountain sun, inspects the withering leaves.

② 風舞茶菁
A worker spreads the tea onto a tarp for the outdoor withering process.

③ 風舞茶菁
The thrown tea leaves dance and flow in the wind.

④ 室內萎凋　傳統鐵觀音室外萎凋約30分鐘，即收集茶菁進入室內。
For the indoor withering process, the tea leaves are placed on round bamboo trays and stored in controlled conditions. Traditional outdoor withering takes about 30 minutes. It is then followed by the indoor withering process.

室內萎凋 檢視茶菁，攤平散溫，均衡發酵。
After sunshine withering, the fresh leaves undergo indoor withering at room temperature. Spreading the tea leaves flat on the bamboo trays allows for even oxidation.

① 室內萎凋 記取茶香需得時，發酵過時難追韻。

The oxidation of the leaves draws out the distinct flavor of the Tie Kuan Yin leaves.

② 做菁一 ── 搖菁之後，鮮葉再次攤開竹盤上，並上架靜置發酵。

Shaking the leaves on the bamboo trays in between oxidation and settling also allows a fuller flavor to resurface throughout the leaves.
Dancing the leaves, the workers gently bruise the leaves, releasing more moisture for even fermentation.

③ 做菁二

Now the leaves dance through the air into a bamboo tray which is then placed on the rack.

茶菁初顯紅鑲邊
As the fermentation nears completion, red color begins to
appear on the edges of the leaf.

午後餘暉中，室內攤涼，茶菁輕輕攏合。

Indoor withering involves multiple steps of drying and rolling. These leaves cool after one rolling. The leaves are beginning to soften in the gentle afternoon sun.

竹籠搖菁機

The leaves are bruised in a different way in a bamboo tumbler. Tumbling produces heat in two ways: 1. Friction 2. Generated by the fermentation process.

菁葉入籠搖菁，使葉沿輕微破壞，加快走水，
促進芬香、滋味等有效物質的轉換，
及更均勻的發酵合成。

Leaves are moved from the drying racks to the bamboo tumbler. Here the leaves are bruised to reduce moisture and encourage proper fermentation. When the tea leaves are fermented correctly at room temperature, the wonderful fragrance of Tie Kuan Yin begins to develop.

茶菁靜置、走水、發酵。

Resting and tumbling becomes an intricate dance as the leaves are moved from trays to tumblers and back again. Each rest becomes longer. The best Tie Kuan Yin usually rests four to five times. The judgment of the Tea Master is very important.

茶菁遂漸發酵，葉沿漸紅，體積漸小。

As the leaves wither they become smaller and softer. More leaves fit into each tray at each rest. The distinctive red edge on the leaves continues to develop.

菁葉再入籠搖菁，傳統做法需搖菁四～五次，一搖匀，二搖水，三搖香，四搖紅，五搖看天時。

Indoor withering can take 16-24 hours to complete. Resting and tumbling happens four or five times. The first time is gentle and even bruising. The second tumbling reduces the moisture. The third time the fragrance appears. The fourth time the red edge on the leaf appears. Whether or not there is a fifth time is determined by the weather. Here, the experience and judgment of the Tea Master is all-important.

① 做菁、搖菁、靜置需返復四到五次，時間由短而長，手法由輕而重，
直到綠葉鑲紅邊，菁氣除盡轉為芳香，過程約16～24小時。

As indoor withering continues, the resting period increases in length and the
tumbling becomes more intense. Near the end, the leaf edges turn red and the
fragrance appears. The entire indoor withering process takes about 16-24 hours.

② 弄菁均堆，上架靜置。

The Tea Master dances the leaves preparatory to resting.

③ 三搖香，香氣顯時再靜置。

The Tie Kuan Yin leaves are ready to begin the third tumbling. This
is where the fragrance develops.

傳統鐵觀音之室內萎凋，鮮葉必需堆起一定厚度。發酵程度在35%～40%。

For the third rest the number of leaves in each tray needs to increase. Without a greater density the proper fermentation (35-40% for Tie Kuan Yin) will not occur.

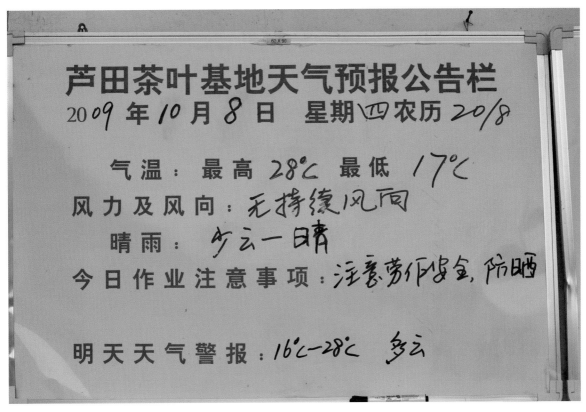

芦田茶叶基地天气预报公告栏
2009 年 10 月 8 日　星期四 农历 20/8

气温：　最高 28℃　最低 17℃
风力及风向：无持续风向
晴雨：　多云一晴
今日作业注意事项：注意劳作安全，防晒

明天天气警报：16℃-28℃　多云

茶廠告示 — 2009年10月8日，寒露，天高氣爽，日照良好，午菁極佳。
The manufacturer's weather board announces a perfect day for creating Tie Kuan Yin oolong. The temperature and humidity are just right and the sky is mostly sunny. The board cautions the workers to wear protective clothing.

殺青
傅止發酵

Stop fermentation

① 茶菁發酵完成，殺菁需即時。
Indoor withering is over. The fresh leaves are now at the end of fermentation at 35-40%.
Fermentation must be stopped immediately for a perfect Tie Kuan Yin.

② 己發酵之茶菁，有著綠葉紅鑲邊。
The red edge on the leaves means it is time to stop fermentation.

③ 傳統殺菁鍋
This is the traditional way to stop fermentation, with a wood-fired machine.

① 木料取火加熱炒鍋
A wood fire heats the pan in traditional stop fermentation equipment.

② 等待炒鍋升溫
The Tea Master waits for the pan to reach the proper temperature for wood-firing.

③ 茶農都有自己的炒鍋設備，茶菁將入鍋殺菁。
At the end of indoor withering, the Tea Master prepares the leaves for stop fermentation.

① 茶菁已完成殺菁下鍋

At the end of stop fermentation, the leaves are removed. The Tea Master inspects the results.

② 許師傅20歲開始學製茶，于今已有25年的經驗，为了茶葉成品市場上好賣，他正捶打剛殺菁的鮮葉，去除黃邊，避免茶湯色泛紅，市場現今流行青綠湯色。去除黃邊的鐵觀音，葉沿破碎如鋸口，已無外形，遑論色美。

Mr. Xu, the Tea Master, hits the leaves to partially break them, making it easier to remove the yellow pieces, leaving green leaves. Green leaves sell better in the market but the broken leaves are not so pretty. Master Xu began learning to make tea at age 20. Now he has 25 years experience.

剛下鍋的茶菁在攤涼
Fermentation has been stopped. Now the hot leaves must be spread out and cooled.

現代化瓦斯氣燃料的殺菁鍋設備
Modern stop fermentation equipment is gas-powered instead of wood-fired.

茶菁在殺菁鍋中舞動
Hot leaves dance inside a modern stop fermentation machine.

① 茶菁入鍋
A Tea Master puts fresh tea leaves into a gas-powered stop fermentation machine.

② 測試鮮葉溫度，判斷下鍋時間。
The young-looking Tea Master is very experienced. She puts her hand inside the blazing hot machine to properly judge when to end stop fermentation. Tea making is an art.

③ 茶菁下鍋
Fermentation is stopped and the Tea Master collects the leaves in a bamboo tray.

① 攤涼已殺菁的鮮葉
At the end of stop fermentation the hot tea leaves are left to cool.

② 鮮葉捶打機後，篩去黃片再進行包揉。
Selecting the final leaves, a worker separates the green leaf from the yellow pieces.

③ 鮮葉捶打機，除鮮葉沿的黃片。
An automatic hitting machine makes it easier to separate the yellow pieces but the finished product is not as pretty.

解塊
圍揉

Rolling and Separating

① 團揉一　團揉是鐵觀音外形、滋味產生的關健之一，團揉先是包揉後解塊，再包揉再解塊，需反覆的進行十幾次，外形穩定後才再進行初焙，每個茶團約5公斤重，時間需4小時以上，，現在有團揉機與解塊機可代替傳統人工，但還是極耗體力的工作.
The first rolling: This process is essential to the creation of traditional and authentic Tie Kuan Yin oolong tea. Rolling leads to the beautiful shape of the finished tea and contributes to the wonderful and unique flavor. Rolling compresses the tea into a ball shape of about 5 kilos in weight. The ball is then separated. This is followed by compression again. The cycle of compress-separate, compress-separate is repeated about 20-30 times. A machine is used to help with the compression, but even then, this job requires powerful muscles and firm internal qi.

② 團揉二
The rolling process begins by shaping the tea using a cotton over-wrap.

③ 團揉三
The cotton is used to form the ball shape.

④ 團揉四
Now the compression of the tea is started by hand.

⑤ 團揉五
The Tea Master twists the over-wrap tighter and tighter.

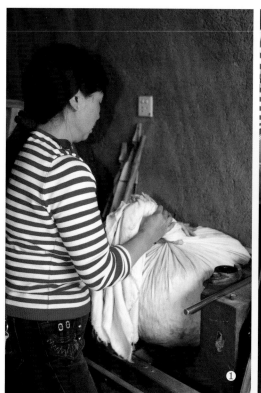

④

① 團揉六 上機攪緊之一 ，鮮葉在包內，相互緊纏成捲形。
A rolling machine is used to achieve maximum compression of the fresh leaves.

② 團揉七 上機攪緊之二，攪勁憑手感與經驗，過與不及皆不中。
The Tea Master flexes her muscles using a metal bar to compress the tea. Her experience is important here. She must feel the force through the bar. Too tight and the ball will explode. Not tight enough and the tea will not become the best.

③ 團揉八 上機攪緊之三，纏住中心點，盤回尾端固定。
Finding the center, balancing yin and yang. At the end of compression, the bar must be centered atop the ball. The tail of the cotton over-wrap must come out to the end of the bar. When balance is attained, a perfect tea is assured.

④ 團揉九 鮮葉團揉成球形，內含物質也在充份放釋、融合。
At the end of the first compression the over-wrap is removed and the ball is revealed. The high pressure inside the ball forces liquid goodness from the fresh leaves, dispersing it throughout the ball. The essences mingle.

① 解塊 散開鮮葉，此時鮮葉已略成捲曲。
The Tea Master begins the first separation. The ball comes apart. The leaves are just beginning to display the twist that is a distinguishing feature of Tie Kuan Yin.

② 再團揉一 累了！換人再進行，不能停！
The compress-separate cycle cannot stop. The first Tea Master needs a rest. Her Tea Master husband continues without losing a beat.

③ 再團揉二 鮮葉尚未緊結，需努力！
The Tea Master begins the second compression by placing the separated leaves into the cloth-lined basket.

④ 再團揉三
The rolling continues with the aid of the machine.

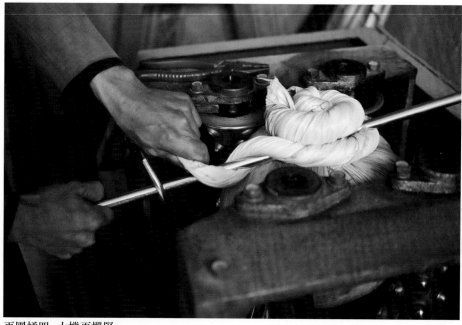

再團揉四　上機再攪緊
Internal power and external strength are both employed as the rolling continues. The second ball is smaller and more of the over-wrap must be coiled on top. Notice the flexing of the Tea Master's powerful hands.

再團揉五　團揉機以360度旋轉，並適度加壓。
A second machine presses and rolls the formed ball.

① 再團揉六　包揉體積正慢慢縮小。
Pressing and rolling, the ball grows smaller.

② 纏
The ball is rolled tight in what might be called "silk reeling." At the end of the rolling and twisting, the ball is locked, it is tight, the tea cannot move.

③ 緊
The balls are tight, the tea is contained and firm.

④ 結
The over-wrap has been twisted tight until it forms a top-knot.

千錘百鍊草中英
Hard work and repetition creates a hero. Strength, balance, and repetition create a superior tea.

靜置後再解塊
The ball rests before the separate-compress cycle begins again.

① 初期團揉較鬆鮮葉易解開
  The first separation. The leaves are not yet so curled and the ball is not yet so tight. Separation is not yet so difficult.

② 外形漸捲曲
  At the end of the first separation the leaves begin to show their distinctive twist.

③ 得心應手
  Creating Tie Kuan Yin for 25 years, the Tea Master smiles with delight as he feels a splendid tea coming to life beneath his skilled hands.

脫胎換骨

As the compress-separate process continues, the ball begins to acquire character. The color of the leaves change, the shape of the leaves change, and the ball becomes more defined.

緊結成形

A beautiful ball shape emerges from the hard work of the Tea Masters.

寶光青瑩
Inside the separator, the ball of tea leaves waits in jade and emerald beauty.

鮮葉青光流動
As the ball grows tighter, human hands can no longer separate the leaves and a machine must be employed. The leaves twirl inside the separator, spinning and flashing with color like the Northern Lights in miniature.

得力助手
Two Tea Masters, married and working together. Two become as one. She exults in the skills of her husband in his prime.

與君共舞
The dance of the Tea Masters. Knowing each other and knowing their art, two Tea Masters, husband and wife, work together and move together. No wasted movement.

細心呵護
A superior tea is the result of many factors. The Tea Masters treat the tea leaves as they would their own children, gently and with respect.

綠之舞 ― 鮮葉解塊之後倒出
Tea leaves dance in the air, a waterfall of green.

初焙揀梗
室視茶質

First dry, Remove stems ,
Tasting the tea

完成團揉的毛茶，猶帶梗技。

At the end of rolling, the leaves now have their distinctive curl and there are still many stems. This tea is sometimes called Mao Cha, "First Tea." It has many stems and is very perishable, but when brewed, it often has an incredible fragrance. Drying is next.

① 茶菁上架待焙
The rolling process is finished and the leaves are stacked in bamboo trays to begin the drying.

② 茶菁烘焙室
Family-owned Tie Kuan Yin processing often uses custom-built gas driers for the firing process.

③ 傳統炭焙籠之一
First dry uses gas. Then the stems are removed. Next, the tea leaves are dried in the old manner with a charcoal fire below the bamboo basket.

④ 傳統炭焙籠之二
Tie Kuan Yin leaves are charcoal fired.

⑤ 傳統炭焙籠之三
This is traditional charcoal firing in bamboo baskets.

① 現代烘焙室
The second and final firing is sometimes done the modern way with these electric dryers.

② 鐵觀音初焙之後需揀梗，去老葉，近日市場上流行的輕焙綠觀音要求更高，一斤毛茶淨挑之後只得六兩，工夫之多不亞於繡花，耐心要求猶如禪定。當知此茶得來不易，猶如盤中珍寶，多加愛惜。
Truly fine tea requires patience. After the first drying, stems are removed by hand. The very best tea is the result of care and focus.

③ 茶都揀梗之一　在產茶旺季，但見安溪茶鄉，人人勤奮，處處揀梗，蔚為一景。
During the Tie Kuan Yin harvest in Anxi, people can be seen everywhere, removing stems from the best tea.

茶都檢梗之二　2009年5月1日午後，日暖風清，茶都迴廊檢梗和樂融融。
May 1, 2009 in Anxi. The weather is warm and a nice breeze is blowing. Removing the stems can be a family affair. Happy conversation punctuates the work.

茶都檢梗之三，右邊是待檢梗的毛茶。

Old and new, as a cellular telephone sits in the middle of traditionally processed tea. Superior tea is always made in a clean environment. Two piles of tea, one with the stems, one without.

審試剛殺菁的毛茶培

A Tea Master does not wait until the end to taste the tea. It is tasted all throughout the process so adjustments can be made to produce the finest tea. These leaves will be tasted just before the first rolling. The flavor is not perfect yet. The Tea Masters must sample as they go.

浸泡中的毛茶培，光潤鮮活，滿室生香。

Before the first firing, after stop fermentation, the leaves are in a gaiwan, a traditional porcelain cup used for tea brewing, ready for tasting. These leaves are green and shining with life, with qi. This shows that stop fermentation was done correctly.

現代審評室

Finished Tie Kuan Yin waits to be tasted in a modern tasting room.

開湯聞香 A Tea Master tests the tea. Smell the fragrance, inspect the leaves, taste the tea.

盖碗工夫杯审茶
Tea tasting gongfu style, pouring tea from a gaiwan.

重焙火之茶葉
After the second firing , this time using a heavy charcoal fire,
a very traditional Tie Kuan Yin is ready for tasting. Notice
the darkness of the leaf.

① 蓋碗工夫杯審茶

小蓋碗審評鐵觀音毛茶，蓋碗約180cc，置茶量約7-10克，沖入沸水，過濾茶湯，先看湯色，再聞香氣，後品佳茗，香、甘、滑、重之喉韻更需細心品啜。

Mao Cha tea testing uses a small gaiwan, about 6 oz, with 7-10 grams of tea leaf. Boiling water covers the tea which is then poured through a strainer for clarity. The Tea Master judges the color, then the fragrance, then the taste. The Tea Master evaluates fragrance, sweet-lingering, smoothness-no astringency, and substance-having an authoritative presence in the mouth.

② 輕焙火之茶葉

Finished Tie Kuan Yin ready for tasting. This is the result of light charcoal firing, a traditional flowery Tie Kuan Yin. The leaves are greener than the more heavily oxidized fragrant Tie Kuan Yin.

③ 輕焙火之茶湯

After the finish of charcoal firing, a gongfu cup of traditional Tea Kuan Yin is ready to be tasted.

① 審視沖泡後之葉底。
A Tea Master looks closely at the wet leaf, judging the quality, the color.

② 鐵觀音乾茶
煙巒秀色草中英，千柔百轉化香茗，
誰能品啜汝辛苦，一顆一粒聚精紳。

Finished Tie Kuan Yin, 35-40% fermented, inspired a poem by me. English cannot exactly reflect the Chinese meaning.
"The generous mountain brings us such a beautiful tea leaf.
One thousand rollings, one hundred twists create a heavenly tea.
Who can taste the true effort made to produce this?
Each piece of tea holds a world of energy and focus."
Jason C.S. Chen

① 香氣是鐵觀音重要的特質
The Tea Master tests the fragrance. Fragrance is very important for a superior Tie Kuan Yin.

② 輕焙火之茶葉底
Admire the leaves. Light charcoal fired Tie Kuan Yin after brewing and tipped out of the gaiwan. Part of gongfu tea is examining the brewed leaves.

③ 綠葉紅鑲邊是鐵觀音做菁的基本要求，一搖勻，二搖水，三搖香，四搖紅，五搖看天時，此圖是四紅六綠，綠腹紅鑲邊正宗做法鐵觀音之葉底，可惜懂此調者漸稀。
The first bamboo basket rolling makes the water in the leaf even. The second rolling makes the water slowly come out. The third rolling brings out the fragrance. The fourth rolling creates the distinctive red rim around the edge of the leaf. If the weather is rainy or cloudy, a fifth rolling may be required. This Tie Kuan Yin is 35-40% fermented. These brewed leaves show off the beautiful Red Heart Peach color around the green leaf indicating genuine, authentic and traditional Tie Kuan Yin.

松林打石泠山泉，濤聲瀟瀟沏佳茗；
慕然回首尋茶人，七品音韻詠奇香。

This beautiful tea inspires a poem.
"Today the water is good. It comes
from the faraway mountains.
And now the water is ready to brew
a fine cup of tea.
I came from the west and was
leaving Anxi,
But the special fragrance drew me
back."
Jason C.S. Chen

滿園山色藏不住，舉世同讚鐵觀音。
Red, green, yellow, and brown: the beautiful colors of the mountain are reflected in this Tie Kuan Yin. Tie Kuan Yin is beloved throughout the world.

五紅五綠，綠腹紅鑲邊正宗做法之鐵觀音葉底。
A special Tie Kuan Yin, oxidized between 45% and 50%, producing colors half-green, half-red.

尋尋覓有伯樂
In the Anxi market, everyone looks for a special Tie Kuan Yin for themselves.

真空7克小包裝
Seven gram, air-tight portion packs of Tie Kuan Yin.

Teamaster from
Anxi county

感德茶農 — 許太太
Tea Master and tea farmer, Ms. Xu of Gande mountain, produces a fine Tie Kuan Yin oolong.

安溪感德 許經福先生 — 25年製茶經驗

Mr. Xu of Gande mountain is a Tea Master with 25 years experience creating a superb Tie Kuan Yin.

堯陽茶農 王先生

Mr. Wang, Tea Master and tea farmer at Yao Yang mountain is an expert in Tie Kuan Yin.

高溪茶莊 蘇旭東先生
Mr. Xu, owns a Tea Store in Anxi Tea Market called
Kao Xi Cha Chuang.

感德 採茶女
An experienced tea picker at Gande mountain.

樂在其中
The joy of tea, removing the stems.

高溪茶莊 蘇太太
Ms. Su at Anxi Tea Market, working at
Kao Xi Cha Chuang tea store.

春池茶莊 陳先生
Mr. Chen, owner of Spring Pond Tea Shop at Anxi Tea Market.

安溪茶都 王小姐
Ms. Wang picking the tea stems at Anxi Tea Market.

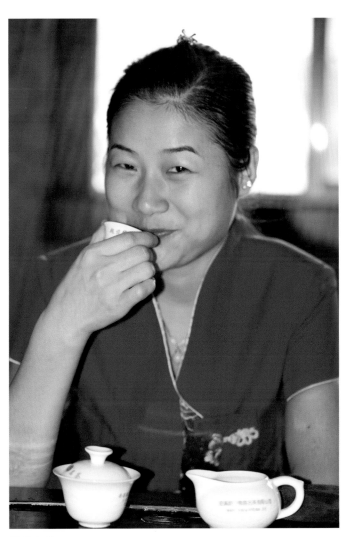

品茗之樂

Happiness is drinking a good cup of Tie Kuan Yin.

魏蔭茶業 魏月德 先生 魏氏鐵觀音第九代傳人

Mr. Wei, owner of Wei Yin Tea Company, is 9th generation descendant of Wei Yin, founder of the Tie Kuan Yin variety.

做菁高手三人行
Indoor Withering professionals.

① 閒暇時光
Taking a break and playing at string art.

② 蘆田茶廠 王廠長
Mr. Wang, General Manager of Lu Tian Tea Facility.

③ 八馬茶業 王文禮 先生 王氏鐵觀音第十三代傳人
Mr. Wang, owner of Eight Horse Tea Company in Anxi. He is 13th generation in the Wang family. His ancestor brought Tie Kuan Yin to Emperor Qinlong.

安溪茶鄉紀行
鐵觀音茶之反思

2009年10月8日，晴，秋高氣爽，農曆八月二十日，節氣寒露，寒露前後三天，正是鐵觀音秋茶採製最佳時間，這天我又回到鐵觀音茶的故鄉—安溪（Anxi）安溪縣位于中國福建省東南境，隸屬泉州市，總面積3057平方公里，總人口108萬人。五代南唐就置縣，宋朝始稱安溪，全縣位于戴雲山脈東南方，平均高度400公尺，氣候屬亞熱帶，年均氣溫16-20℃，年降雨量1800mm以上，夏日長而濕熱，冬季短而無嚴寒，俗謂：四季有花常見雨，嚴冬無雪有雷聲。縣境西北地區羣山環抱，平均高度800公尺，千米以上山峰140座，最高峰1600米，地質屬微酸性紅壤，非常適合茶樹生長，現今茶園總面積有6700公頃，自古至今均以茶鄉聞名于世。

今年已是第二次來到安溪，上次在春茶季節與蘇旭東先生、感德茶農許經福先生，一起製作傳統的鐵觀音，並續2008年的試作的經驗，希望能保留原有的工序優點，同時兼顧市場的喜愛，試作結果成品：外形緊結翠綠，蘭花清香，茶湯金黃帶綠，喉韻甘醇。分送茶友品嚐之後，得到許多鼓勵，我們決定秋茶季節再試一次，因為秋茶香高，有不同于春茶滋味甘醇之處。

蘇旭東先生也是鐵觀音的茶迷，他在安溪茶都有間風評頗佳的茶莊，他也感受到鐵觀音茶傳統工藝的沒落。常說：近五年來新入行的年青茶農，已不知道傳統搖菁、萎凋發酵的方法，甚至認為綠葉紅鑲邊是做壞的茶菁。于是有志一同，尋找有經驗的茶農，試作傳統優點的鐵觀音。

猶記1998年第一次前往安溪，交通遠不如現在方便，曠日費時：安溪再前往西坪-鐵觀音的發源地，山路更加崎嶇，路面石頭林立，非常顛頗，往返就要四～五小時；但是在蘇旭東先生的帶領，拜訪了許多西坪茶廠及國營安溪茶廠，品嚐了許多不同等級、風格的鐵觀音；清香型-蘭香優雅、馥郁悠長，炭焙濃香型-異香撲鼻、喉韻甘美。從此成為鐵觀音茶迷，也對鐵觀音能風行數百年，揚名國際有更深的了解。當時安溪雖地偏路遠，山區茶農都能遵循傳統製茶，擁有舉世無雙的好茶。

但是千喜年之後，中國經濟逾加澎勃，社會消費能力快速增長，安溪交通也日益便捷，全國各省市茶商蜂踴而至，爭相採購，慢慢地形成鐵觀音三個災難。

一、製茶者再也無法靜心，依經驗法則製出好茶。

產茶季節，茶商湧入茶山，山中小徑，車阻于道入夜不息，山村喧嘩如不夜之城，爭相親訪製茶名手，各以自己對茶的了解，進行訂茶，綠茶區來者，要口味清爽、花香的鐵觀音；銷售高價台灣烏龍茶獲利者，要求製作類似輕發酵的鐵觀音，以冲泡出青綠湯色，並以誇稱品質，哄抬價格；因此各個茶商身懷巨款，坐守茶農家中，中夜都不肯散去，毛茶初成，若合符他們的要求—"輕發酵、葉面高香、外形、湯色青綠。"就爭相競價搶茶，茶農則自滿于人氣旺盛，依高利原則，儘量做出他們要的茶品，在這名利氣氛引導之下，當今青綠鐵觀音已成主流，再無人細究傳統的特色及優點，安溪鐵觀音陷入空前的迷思。

二、傳統室內萎潤、殺菁技術的流失。

良好的交通網，促使現代化家電大量運入山村，許多茶農為了節省人力，求取青綠湯色茶品，吻合市場的需求。在茶菁室內萎潤時，放棄傳統、自然方式，另走捷徑；萎潤室改用室內空調機，同時薄攤茶葉，加速走水，茶菁更不敢做菁、搖菁及沃堆發酵。事實上這樣的茶菁發酵只有15%以下，葉面香氣雖高，卻不優雅，不久即散，冷香則無；茶湯滋味雖清爽微甘，卻無喉韻，三次冲泡之後即如清水，遑論七品猶餘香。

又鐵觀音茶種，鮮葉厚實，如絹似紙，如果沒有足夠的搖青、走水、靜置、沃堆發酵，使其有效發酵到35%～40%，鮮葉中的有益物質，無法轉變成芳香甘醇，而且發酵不足茶菁製成的鐵觀音，飲之性寒且利，多飲噁心有飢餓感，傷及脾胃不益身心健康。

三、團採技術不到位，外形改變的迷失。

鐵觀音茶向來以形美、色雅、香高、味醇著名于世，乾茶落壺叮噹有聲，身骨勻重著稱，讚之：美如觀音重似鐵。

但現今茶農為了追求青綠外形及茶湯，鮮葉在殺菁之後，另又包裹茶菁用力摔打，更甚者用摔打機器，除去黃片及綠葉紅鑲邊，造成葉形破碎如鋸口，因此部份發酵才會有的音韻不復見；在包揉、團揉時更不敢做足，以致外觀不成形，失去卷曲緊結，厚實勻淨的特色，也失去促使茶質轉變均勻、柔順耐泡的機會。

又毛茶完成後又耗費大量的人力，追求揀梗盡淨，成品完成後只見翠綠有如綠茶片，泡之、嚐之則尚不如傳統綠茶，此不禁惋惜鐵觀音數百年精湛、完美、獨到的工藝，而失去形美、音韻、滋味的烏龍綠葉片能稱之鐵觀音嗎？

近年來安溪部份有識茶商，也開始重視這種偏離鐵觀音傳統的現象，加強宣傳鐵觀音茶品茗方法，並在製作上遂漸回歸傳統工藝，保留傳統清香型、碳焙濃香型的鐵觀音茶韻，同時與市場需求做更好的融合，期望引領更多的愛好者，進入真正鐵觀音茶的世界。

Anxi County Diary

October 8, 2009 is a beautiful Autumn day. The sun is shining. The Chinese calendar is August 20. The Chinese calendar has 24 seasons. This is Han Lu season, the first day the first drop of water in the morning becomes cold. Three days before and after Han Lu for a total of 7 days is the best time to harvest Tie Kuan Yin. On this day I return to Anxi county.

Anxi county is located in southeast Fujian province. The county belongs to Quanzhou city. Total area 3,057 square km. The population is 1,080,000. The city began very early, about 1,000 years ago during the Tang Dynasty. Anxi county was named during the Song Dynasty, 800 years ago. The entire county is located SE of Dai Yun Mountain. The Average altitude is 1,200 feet. The climate zone is subtropical. The average temperature is 16-20 celcius.

The average rainfall is 1,800 mm per year. In the summer, the days are long, humid, and hot. The winter is short and mild. The local people say "All four seasons have flowers and it always rains." In the winter there is no snow and sometimes there is thunder. In Anxi county NW there are many high mountains. This is where most of the tea grows. The average altitude is 2,400 feet. Most of the mountains exceed 3,000 feet in height. The highest mountain is 5,000 feet. The land is red and the soil is slightly sour. This is very good for tea growing. Today the total tea growing area in Anxi is 6,700 hectares. This area has been famous for its tea for many, many years.

This is my second visit to Anxi in 2009. My first visit was in the spring. During that trip I created a special Tie Kuan Yin with my friend Mr. Xu, who is a tea farmer. That first visit in 2009, we worked together and continued our 2008 experience. We had one big wish. We wished we can keep the traditional qualities of Tie Kuan Yin, and also make a special fragrance, color, and taste for the new market, the next generation. The job is not easy. We worked hard for two years but the results are pretty good. In spring and fall we had a good project. We made the tea in a lovely shape, twisted and tight. The fragrance is a beautiful orchid. The tea color is light golden-yellow and green. The lingering is sweet. I have shared this tea with many tea lovers. Everyone likes it. So we decided to try this again during fall production. Fall Tie Kuan Yin has the most fragrance.

Mr. Su is also a Tie Kuan Yin tea lover. He has his own shop in the Anxi tea market. This shop is called Gao Xi Cha Zhuang. This a popular tea shop in Anxi market. He also has a feeling that the traditional Tie Kuan Yin skills are declining and the younger generation does not understand this. He always says "The younger tea makers, those with five years or less experience, do not understand how to make traditional Tie Kuan Yin. The older generation knows." The new farmers do not understand rolling or how to do the indoor withering. Sometimes the younger farmer says the 40% oxidized Tie Kuan Yin is damaged leaf because of the smell as it is being processed. We look to the older generation of tea farmers to continue the tradition.

I still remember my first visit to Anxi county in 1998. Transportation to Anxi county was not so convenient. It took an entire day to get from Xiamen to the mountains. From Anxi county to Xiping the mountain road was so rocky riding in the SUV was just like rock and roll. But I had a really good time. Mr. Su gave me some very good leads. We visited several Xiping and Anxi tea facilities. At that time the Anxi facilities belonged to the government. I tasted many different levels of Tie Kuan Yin. Including the flowery style and the charcoal fired style. Orchid fragrance, special fragrance, the lingering was always sweet and beautiful. I fell in love with Tie Kuan Yin on this trip. Then I understood why Tie Kuan Yin had been popular for so many years and throughout the world. At that time Anxi area transportation was very bad and the mountain farmer was poor, but everyone followed the traditions and produced the best tea in the world.

But from 2000, the economy in China began to change dramatically. The economy grew, the consumers became rich, and there was much money to spend. Anxi transportation was also improving. The tea wholesale buyers could now come to Anxi from all over China. Everyone wanted Tie Kuan Yin. Everyone had money and the bidding escalated.

Three troubles for Tie Kuan Yin developed:

1. The tea farmer no longer had the peaceful atmosphere necessary to produce authentic Tie Kuan Yin. Buyers began appearing at the farms during processing season. The mountain road was so tiny, the buyers in their SUV's began causing traffic jams···even at midnight! In small villages in the mountains the crowds were constant. Anxi was becoming like Las Vegas! The buyers were fighting each other to acquire these small farm teas. They went from one farm to the next bidding against one another. The market for Tie Kuan Yin was ravenous and everything was being swallowed up. Each buyer influenced the character of the teas they were buying. If the buyer was from Zhejiang province and used to buying green tea, he would demand green color and green tea fragrance from the Tie Kuan Yin farmer. Some tea buyers became rich selling Taiwanese style oolong, light oolong, 20% oxidized. These buyers asked the farmers to create a light Tie Kuan Yin especially for them. They then sold it as "special" and made even more money. The tea buyers would stay at the farmer's house until midnight; they did not want to go until the Mao Cha was ready. The Mao Cha, "original tea" matched the requirements for a greener Tie Kuan Yin. Then the buyers tried to outbid each other for this greener tea. The farmer was happy with a higher profit. The farmers began following the orders from the buyer and creating whatever the buyers wanted. Now the green Tie Kuan Yin has become a popular style. No one cares about tradition. Authentic and traditional Tie Kuan Yin is in trouble.

2. The traditional indoor withering and stop fermentation skills are being lost. As the transportation improved in the mountains, modern electric equipment came to the mountains, too. Refrigeration, air conditioning, electric tea drying machines···all electric. This also saved labor. The tea farmers began using air conditioning for indoor withering to create a greener Tie Kuan Yin, forgetting the traditional and natural methods. The air conditioning did all of this quickly. With the air conditioning, the thick layers of fresh tea leaves in indoor withering became one layer to accommodate the air conditioning which removed the moisture from the air. The traditional bamboo rolling tumblers were abandoned as was heavy fermentation. They forgot tradition. The new "Tie Kuan Yin" was only oxidized 15% or less. Even fresh leaves have a good fragrance, but it is

not as delicate and gentle as the fragrance of a true, authentic and traditional Tie Kuan Yin. The fragrance of greener Tie Kuan Yin does not last. Good tea must have both a hot and a cold fragrance. The new Tie Kuan Yin has no cold fragrance. Even though the taste is clean and slightly sweet it is only good for 2-3 steepings with a gaiwan, whereas traditional Tie Kuan Yin will be good for 6 or 7 steepings.

3. Traditional Tie Kuan Yin needs 20 or more rollings. Today, the rolling skill of modern producers is not so good. The twist is less, the tightness is reduced. The shape has changed.

Twenty or more rollings are necessary to create the best Tie Kuan Yin shape for four reasons: 1. Beautiful shape. 2. Delicate color. 3. High fragrance. 4. Sweet lingering.

When the traditional Tie Kuan Yin is added to the teapot it makes beautiful music, like a bell. Today's farmer is trying to produce the greener tea for the new Tie Kuan Yin market . Now, the modern farmer after stop fermentation, either by hand or by machine, strikes the fresh leaf to remove the brown ring on its edges that was caused by the stop fermentation process. With the new demand for greener Tie Kuan Yin, the brown ring is considered undesirable. After the hitting, the leaf is broken and only the green parts remain. The leaf has lost its beautiful shape. The edges become jagged or saw-toothed. Today's farmer only rolls the leaves a few times because repeated rolling will make the leaves red, when the farmer perceives only a market for green leaves. With insufficient rolling, the beautiful shape will never appear. Not rolling enough also retards the internal blending.

When the Mao Cha is finished, removing the stems is labor-intensive. Without the twist, more stems must be removed. The result which is stem-less and lightly oxidized, might be more correctly called a "green" tea. One problem, this is not really an authentic Tie Kuan Yin, and it does not even taste as good as a good green tea. A lot of money is spent on this greener Tie Kuan Yin. I feel pity that the delicate, perfect, special Tie Kuan Yin process developed over the past 300 plus years is almost gone. No more beautiful shape, no more beautiful lingering…is this still Tie Kuan Yin?

Today, there remain a few smart tea processors and tea facilities. They are beginning to understand the problem and are moving back to the traditional. They are promoting their traditional and authentic tea so consumers will understand what has been missing. In Anxi, tea farmers still care about tradition and the feelings of the younger generation. I hope tea lovers can enjoy the real world of Tie Kuan Yin.

鐵觀音沖泡方法

沖泡鐵觀音，以紫砂小壺、功夫茶具為上選，並採用山泉好水，滾水備用，先溫壺後置入約鋪滿壺底壺的茶量，再沖水入壺一半，隨即倒出，既用于醒茶，也用于享用鐵觀音獨特的香氣，第二次沖入滾水滿壺，靜置約1分鐘即可倒出在小杯飲用，鐵觀音使用功夫茶具沖泡，清香型可以沖泡5次,炭焙濃音型清香型可以沖泡7次以上。

一般茶壺沖泡，約600cc的茶壺配用7-8克茶葉，浸泡3～5分鐘後飲用，清香型可以沖泡3次，炭焙濃音型清香型可以沖泡5次。

茶師傅自動沖茶杯，置茶量7克，選用好水煮沸加入即可，約三分鐘即沖泡完成，清香型可以沖泡3次以上，炭焙濃音型清香型可以沖泡5次以上。

The perfect cup of Tie Kuan Yin

The traditional way to enjoy this tea is Gongfu style (Kungfu).

Use a small Yixing clay teapot and fill the teapot 10% (7-10 gram) with the tea leaf. Always begin with good boiling water.

During the first steep, in the teapot, rinse the leaf with a small amount of boiling water and let it sit on the leaves for 10 seconds. Pour the water off. Then enjoy the fragrance of the leaves. This is often called "Awakening the Dragon." Always use boiling water 205-210F for this tea. For the second steeping, add the water, then pour the tea after 60 seconds steep time. Serve in small tea cups.

Tie Kuan Yin Oolong Tea can be steeped up to 5-7 times when using the Gongfu method. The tea always has a similar flavor but the aroma changes with each steeping, so please enjoy the fragrance change.

When brewing with a normal tea pot, use 7-8 grams dry leaf. For a twenty ounce tea pot use ten grams tea. Steep 3- 5 minutes. Enjoy 3-5 times.

For the TeaMaster Automatic Tea Brewer® use 7 grams of tea. Add boiling water. In about three minutes your tea will be ready. Enjoy 3-5 times.

鐵觀音製作工序一覽

採茶

曬青(日光萎凋)

做青、搖菁來回重複(室內萎潤) 4-5次

殺菁(停止發酵)

團揉與解塊 來回重複約20次至緊結卷曲成形

初烘焙

審視茶質

檢梗

風選、拼堆精選

碳火低溫復烘焙

茶品檢測

成品包裝

Tie Kuan Yin Oolong Tea: The Process

Tea picking.

Outdoor withering (Sunshine withering).

Indoor withering: Alternate dancing the leaves and tumbling 4-5 times.

Stop fermentation.

Rolling and separating the leaves more than 20 times
until they form a ball or "Dragon" style.

First drying.

Tasting the tea.

Remove the stems

Sorting the leaves, Selecting the Best.

The Final Fire Charcoal Drying

Quality inspection and tea cupping.

Product packaging.

作者

1955年出生台灣，1985年始喜愛茗茶，，1989開始中國茶鄉之旅迄今21年，雖在1991年遷居美國也不曾中斷，1997年移居西雅圖，成立C.C.FINE TEA CORP.（茶馬仕茶業有限公司）為了最佳茶葉品質，致力于中國經營茶園、開發茶具，頻繁前往各地茶區，同時用攝影忠實記錄名種茶原產地茶園風光，及中國茶葉面向世界在技術、設備、包裝上的脫變與成長。

About the Author

Tea Master Jason C.S. Chen was born in Taiwan in 1955. He began to learn the art of tea in 1985. In 1989 he began his tea travels, visiting the finest tea-growing areas in China. Now, Master Chen has been traveling in pursuit of fine tea for 21 years. He moved to Seattle, Washington in 1997 and started his own tea business, C.C. Fine Tea Corporation. The traveling never stopped. To ensure the finest tea quality, Master Chen decided to develop his own tea gardens in China. To enhance the tea lover's enjoyment of the beverage, he invented new accessories. New tea gardens, new tea brewing accessories, this all meant even more time spent on the road in China. Master Chen travelled to the locations where authentic and traditional Chinese tea is grown and processed. He brought with him on his travels, a camera. He kept a photographic record of his progress toward producing the highest quality tea and the best ways to brew and enjoy this tea.

茶山紀行 鳳凰單欉與鐵觀音

攝影及文稿：陳嘉生
英文文稿：Pierce B. Watters
平面設計：汪偉 孫貴軼
編輯概念：汪偉 陳嘉生

A Tea Lover's Travel Diary
Phoenix Single-Bush Oolong Tea
Tie Kuan Yin Oolong Tea

PHOTOGRAPHY AND TEXT：Jason C. S. Chen
ENGLISH TEXT：Pierce B. Watters
GRAPHIC DESIGN：Wang Wei SunGuiYi
CONCEPT：Wang Wei Jason C. S. Chen